Endors

"Creative and wise, ***Recipe for Radiance*** is a guide to radiant living. Dr. Katherine T. Kelly leads you through your personal care recipe planning with wisdom and ease. So, gather your equipment and your ingredients and create your own life-changing recipe for Soul-Full self-care."

– **Janet G Nestor**, MA LPC DCEP, mental health counselor and author of *Pathways to Wholeness and Nurturing Wellness through Radical Self-Care*

"***Recipe for Radiance*** is magnificent. It will guide you through the transformation of recharging your mind, inspiring your soul, and restoring your body. I have learned through this book to develop a self-care plan, a life-long guide for my soul's optimal health. This is a book you do not want to miss."

– **Marsha Stafford**, host of the Been There Done That Radio Show

"As a dietitian, I absolutely love how Dr. Kelly uses the metaphor relating self-care to recipes and cooking in ***Recipe for Radiance.*** Successful cooks become that way from practice and patience. We need the same traits when caring for ourselves. Practicing what has been proven to work and seeing consistent results gives us courage."

– **Krista Kiger,** MA, RD, Certified Health Coach

Recipe for Radiance

KATHERINE T. KELLY, PH.D, M.S.P.H.

WINSTON-SALEM, NC

Soul Health Press books may be ordered through booksellers or by contacting:

Soul Health Press
www.soulhealthpress.com or **www.drkatherinetkelly.com**

Because of the dynamic nature of the internet, any web addresses or links contained in this book may have changed since publication and may no longer be valid.

The author of this book does not dispense medical advice or prescribe the use of any technique as a form of treatment for physical, emotional, or medical problems without the advice of a physician, either directly or indirectly. The intent of the author is only to offer information of the general nature to help you in the quest for emotional and spiritual well-being. In the event you use any of the information in this book for yourself, which is your constitutional right, the author and the publisher assume no responsibility for your actions.

Publisher's Cataloging-in-Publication Data

Names: Kelly, Katherine T., author.
Title: Recipe for radiance : mastering the art and soul of self-care / Katherine T. Kelly, Ph.D, M.S.P.H.
Description: Includes bibliographical references | Winston-Salem, NC: Soul Health Press, 2019.
Identifiers: LCCN 2019902087 | ISBN 978-1-7320489-4-2 (Hardcover) | 978-1-7320489-3-5 (pbk.) | 978-1-7320489-5-9 (ebook)
Subjects: LCSH Soul. | Self-care, Health. | Self-actualization (Psychology) | Stress (Psychology) | Stress management.| BISAC SELF-HELP / Self-Management / Stress Management | HEALTH & FITNESS / Healthy Living
Classification: LCC RA785 .K45 2019 | DDC 616.9/8--dc23

Published 2019
Printed in the United States of America
ISBN: 978-1-7320489-3-5 (sc)
ISBN: 978-1-7320489-4-2 (hc)
ISBN: 978-1-7320489-5-9 (e)

Library of Congress Control Number: 2019902087

Cover illustration and design by Chara Murray, Firefly Designs
Interior layout and design by Deana Riddle, Bookstarter Design

Dedication

To Mom for teaching me the basics of cooking from the time I could stand.

To Dad for believing in all of my wild aspirations.

To your radiant health – now and always.

Contents

An empty lantern provides no light.
Self-care is the fuel that allows your light to shine brightly.

~ Unknown

Acknowledgments

Life is a constant lesson, and the human condition is just one medium through which the Universe works to assist in evolving our soul. I am forever grateful to each and every other soul – animals included – who has touched my life and enhanced my personal journey.

I will always give primary credit for the words I share to the thousands of clients and workshop participants I have had the privilege to know and assist in their healing journeys. My mission is to help you evolve, and as a result of knowing you, I evolve further as well. Thank you.

My deep gratitude also goes to the many authors, teachers, health educators, and spiritual leaders, whether in this world or beyond, whose wisdom facilitates my own evolution. This allows me to advance the evolution of others – a gift I greatly welcome and humbly deliver.

One of the key ingredients to my own radiant health is my connection with the members of my soul group. You know who you are. Read this as a reminder that you are cherished, honored, and very much appreciated. You feed me at the deepest level possible. Thank you from the bottom of my soul to the furthest reach in the Universe.

Special thanks goes to Carol Walsh, friend, suite mate, and master of words. I appreciate your willingness to peruse the pages throughout various stages of this book's development. I also appreciate our frequent recipe swapping and taste-testing when we find those golden gems.

Continued thanks go to Chara Murray, my amazing and visionary graphic artist who gets me and pictorially captures the concepts provided in this book – as well as pretty much everything I have produced in the last twelve years. The "we can conquer the world" title lives strong in my mind, heart, and soul and continues to motivate me to do everything I can to help this world evolve and continue on my own soulful path. Here's to many more adventures before us!

Many thanks go to Carol Hildebrandt, chief wordsmith and editor for stepping in to fine-tune the words before you. Without you, the *Recipe* might have missed several key ingredients. Your swift and magical work is greatly appreciated.

Finally, my gratitude goes to everyone who reads this book and puts to use the thoughts and ideas that will help you to create a more radiant life. In evolving as both a human being and soul, you also participate in the evolution of this planet. Just imagine what this world would be like if each and every soul chose to love and care for themselves enough to live more radiantly! Thank you for investing in yourself, which also invests in the Oneness of all.

A Note from the Author

Do you want to feel more alive? More balanced? Have more energy? Be more radiant? If so, it is time to care for the most important part of you – your *soul.*

To me, self-care *IS* soul care. When we tend to the various aspects of our human lives that need attention, we also care for our innermost ally. But few of us know exactly what we as individuals uniquely need to feel more radiant. Instead, we have ideas about what all of us need to achieve good physical health – frequent exercise and good nutrition with a little bit of relaxation sprinkled in. However, as unique as each of us is, we all need more than this to really feed and sustain us. We each require our own personal combination of soul-care activities – our unique recipe that more fully fits our individual needs and more richly nourishes and balances our life.

I inadvertently discovered the primary ingredient in my own recipe for ultimate self-care years ago when I was in graduate school, training to become a psychologist. It was a difficult time in my life. Grad school is stressful enough in and of itself, but several other life circumstances were impacting my overall well-being at the time. Having discovered some deep deceit and manipulation on the part of my spouse shortly after we married, I found myself in an unhealthy marriage. A family member was struggling with serious mental health issues. I was still grieving the loss of my father the year before. To top it off, several close supports and friendships were fading due to overall life circumstances.

My husband and I had recently moved into a home together. I had just started the Ph.D. program, and nothing looked or felt the same as it had just a few short months before. My whole world felt like it had been scrambled, and all the change and stress had begun to take a major toll not only on my physical and emotional health, but also on my soul's well-being. Yet, having just started the doctoral program, I felt pulled to stay focused on my training.

I sat on the couch one night trying to read a chapter for the next day's class. I read the same few pages over and over again, not absorbing any of the information. I kept trying to focus, only to get more frustrated that nothing was sticking in my brain. It seemed like all the information just seeped out as soon as it entered.

I realized the extreme stress from my preoccupation with other life events was derailing any chance I had of getting through the chapter. I knew I needed to do something to release the surging discomfort. So even though I loathed evening workouts, I decided to go to the gym. Usually I preferred to exercise right after classes or work so I could settle in afterward to study. However, that particular evening I knew I needed to move and to burn out my nervous, disturbed energy so I could focus in on and preserve the one thing I was doing at the time just for me – the education that would take me into my future. I had to go to the gym!

I got there around 7:30 that evening. At the time, my typical workout was a fifteen-minute climb on the Stairmaster, followed by twenty to thirty minutes of moderate walking on a treadmill. While climbing the stairs, I realized my heavy, scrambled feeling wasn't going away. When I stepped onto the treadmill, I started out at my usual pace, only to realize after a few minutes this too wasn't going to be enough. So I did something that was unlike me – I cranked up the treadmill and began to jog. I've never been a runner, choosing to do fairly intense and longer walks instead. But this night was different. I needed to do something else to break through the anxious barrier that was weighing me down.

I increased the speed on the machine until I was running at a steady pace. Huffing and puffing, I pushed myself for seven or so intense minutes until the magic happened. The overwhelming blanket of pressure was starting to lift, easing my stress, as if an internal valve had been released. I could literally feel the unwanted force lifting from me at a slow, but much welcomed rate.

I ran for several more minutes until I could feel myself become more balanced and focused. I slowed down to walk for a few minutes more. Once I felt back to normal – or what passed for normal at that time in my life – I ended the workout, made my way home, settled back onto the couch, and resumed my studies. My mind was clear, and I was able to complete my reading quickly. I even got a decent night's rest before my class the next day.

That was the night I realized self-care would be my salvation. It became my magic wand, casting a spell of well-being that has helped me through every day of my life since. That was the very night I transformed my dark and heavy outlook about life into a much brighter and more empowered future. I found the radiance I needed in that moment to get me to the next. The realization came that if we listen deeply to the voice within our soul, it tells us exactly what we need in order to not just survive, but to thrive.

It was a powerful night – one that set my life upon a trail of discovery and helped me identify other key ingredients that would, without fail, get me through any challenging event. As time went on, I added other primary elements. I explored the more fluid aspects of daily self-care that are important and unique to who I am – what I call the broth. I experimented with and chose the spices – those things that season my life, flavor my life path, and enhance my experience of day-to-day living. All of these ingredients became my go to soul-care activities and remain the ingredients to this day that make up my own personal recipe for radiant living.

And now I want to help you discover, create, and savor your own ***Recipe for Radiance***.

Chapter One

Recipe for Radiance

> *"Caring for your body, mind, and spirit is your greatest and grandest responsibility. It's about listening to the needs of your soul and then honoring them."*
>
> ~ Kristi Ling

Simply stated, your soul is the essence of who you are. It is the hub and nucleus of every action, behavior, thought, and emotion. It houses your inherent wisdom about what you want and need for optimal living. Your soul constantly monitors how you take care of yourself in your human life so it can continue to thrive, grow, and evolve. This nonstop assessment tells you how you can both create and maintain your radiance – that feeling you seek as you strive to achieve health and wellness. When you don't attend to your outer circumstances you also neglect your soul. This can seriously dim your inner light.

The Recipe for Radiance: Mastering the Art and Soul of Self-Care is designed to help you create your own ultimate, life-long guide for optimal health – for your *soul health.* Although consciously tending to one's own well-being is relatively new, the trend toward a proactive and well-balanced lifestyle is nothing less than a positive – and essential – one. In fact, it is the key to both radiant health and conscious evolution.

As far as we know, we are the only species that can consciously decide to make our lives better. However, when asked, most people can't fully describe what it takes to keep them afloat, let alone identify what helps them feel more radiant. While it's important to care for yourself during or after a stressful event, it's essential that you establish an ongoing self-care plan that sets the foundation for your overall soul health as well as restores you when your internal resources are depleted. If radiant living is what you want, this book will provide you with the tools to help you get there.

Your *Recipe for Radiance* will help you:

Restore your body...

Recharge your mind...

Inspire your soul... and,

Transform your life...

In the thirty years I've been in practice, I've discovered the cooking metaphor is an incredibly effective tool to help my clients as they explore the concepts of ultimate self-care, soul health, and radiant living. Therefore, it is the metaphor I have used in this book. It will guide you to your inner wisdom that already knows so well how to satisfy and satiate your hungry soul. Creating and following your own recipe for radiant living will, without fail, ensure you practice lifelong self-care.

The three essential types of ingredients you need to create your *Recipe for Radiance* will be explored throughout this book. While other books stress the importance of self-care for health and wellness, this book provides you with the instructions to create your own unique recipe that will not only result in good physical and emotional health, but will also nourish your soul for the rest of your life. You will explore your own personal blocks to self-care as well as determine exactly what you need to perfect your recipe for soul health and radiant living. Never before have you explored self-care in such an in-depth way.

How to Use this Book

The ***Recipe for Radiance: Mastering the Art and Soul of Self-Care*** is written as your guidebook for creating your unique master soul-care plan for radiant living. You will find many activities and lists of things to ponder in each chapter. I encourage you to purchase a notebook or journal to use as you work your way through the book. It will become your cookbook for what does and doesn't work in your life - your very own cookbook for the soul. Much like any good cook, you will need to take notes as you experiment and create your ideal and unique recipe for life. My actual recipe binder is full of sticky notes scribbled with recipe ideas, notes about added and omitted ingredients, and instructions for particular cooking techniques. My personal soul-care journal is much the same.

As you read this book, you will find yourself reflecting upon what has and hasn't worked in the past with regard to your self-care and how you approached it. You will also imagine what you want to have happen in the future to enhance your overall well-being. This is what all master chefs do with their meals. They constantly reflect on their past creations and imagine new ones. Having a notebook or journal at your side as you read this book will allow you to perfect your soul-care plan along the way. Whether you purchase a fancy journal or use a simple notebook it will become your personalized cookbook filled with your recipes for self-care. Remember, self-care *IS* soul care. Only when you identify your own unique set of ingredients for your soul-sustaining health do you also create your most radiant life.

Congratulations on committing to your ultimate self-care — your *SOUL* care!

Chapter Two

Self-Care Path to Radiant Living

> *"Self-care is how you take your power back."*
> ~ Lalah Delia

Why don't we take care of ourselves like we know we should? What keeps us from following through with healthy behaviors even when risking poor health? How often do we opt out of a self-care activity in order to take care of others instead?

The research is clear. Those who actively participate in healthy and nurturing behavior have ***LESS***

depression,
stress,
anxiety, and
physical illness.

They also have ***MORE***

energy,
optimism,
life/job/relationship satisfaction, and,
most important of all, JOY.

If all of this is true, what keeps you from caring for yourself and your soul? Below are the most common reasons people give when asked this question. How many of these have you said about your own self-care?

- "I don't have time."
- "Others come first."
- "I don't deserve it."
- "Others need it more."
- "I'm too busy."
- "I'm too tired."
- "I don't know what to do to take care of myself."
- "I feel guilty."
- "I'd feel selfish."

Several studies have measured health beliefs and self-care activities, including research about who does and doesn't follow through. However, none of us needs an experiment to admit we all could benefit from more consistent acts of self-preservation.

What Goes in Sometimes Leaks Out

What you will read about next is a little activity I do with folks to illustrate what happens when the amount of energy you put out to the world exceeds what comes in. Imagine a clay pot that represents your vessel of life.

It holds the amount of energy that you must have to sustain you from day-to-day. Although we all want our vessel of life to remain full, we all leak our life force in direct relation to the number of stressors going on in our lives.

Grab your notebook and take a minute to list all the things and people in your life that are draining you right now:

Work:	What aspects of your job drain your energy?
Home:	What specific parts of your home life exhaust you?
Health:	How do health concerns deplete your life force?
Relationships:	Which of your relationships are life-enhancing vs. life-diminishing?
Finances:	Is your financial foundation as strong as you would like it to be? Is it a source of support or stress?
Other:	What else drains your overall energy?

Now imagine your vessel leaking energy proportionate to these stressors. Does your work life represent a crack, a fissure, or a hole in your vessel? How would you illustrate the leakage of energy your home life creates? Your health? Your relationships? Your finances? Other energy drains?

The more your vessel leaks, the more you need to fill it up to maintain some sort of balance. If you don't actively replace the energy you release, you become more susceptible to illness. The American Stress Institute has studied this concept for decades to help measure the direct impact particular life stressors have on the likelihood of physical illness (including stress, depression, and anxiety). The Holmes-Rahe Social Readjustment Scale is the best known assessment for vulnerability to illness as related to life stressors.

Take a few minutes to complete the inventory below by adding up the Life Change Units (LCU's) associated with the stressors you have experienced in the last year. If a certain item has occurred more than once in the last twelve months, multiply the LCU's by the number of times it has occurred and then add it to your total. (For example, if you have moved residences more than once in the last year, you will add 20 LCU's to the total for each time you have moved.)

Holmes-Rahe Social Readjustment Scale

Rank	Life event	Life Change Unit
1.	Death of spouse	100
2.	Divorce	73
3.	Separation from mate or spouse	73
4.	Death of a close family member	63
5.	Detention in jail or other institution	63

Rank	Life event	Life Change Unit
6.	Major personal injury or illness	53
7.	Marriage	50
8.	Being fired/let go from work	47
9.	Reconciliation with mate or spouse	45
10.	Retirement	45
11.	Major change in health or behavior of a family member	44
12.	Pregnancy	40
13.	Sexual difficulties	39
14.	Gaining of new family member (birth, adoption, older adult)	39
15.	Major business readjustment	39
16.	Major change in financial state	38
17.	Death of close friend	37
18.	Changing to different line of work	36
19.	Change in number of arguments with spouse	35
20.	Taking on a mortgage (new home/business)	31
21.	Foreclosure of mortgage or loan	30
22.	Major changes in responsibilities at work	29
23.	Son or daughter leaving home	29
24.	Trouble with in-laws	29
25.	Outstanding personal achievement	28
26.	Spouse beginning or ceasing work outside the home	26
27.	Beginning or ceasing formal schooling	26
28.	Major change in living conditions (new home, remodeling, etc.)	25

Rank	Life event	Life Change Unit
29.	Revision of personal habits (health/personal development)	24
30.	Trouble with boss	23
31.	Major changes in work hours or conditions	20
32.	Change in residence	20
33.	Changing to a new school	20
34.	Major change in type or amount of recreation	19
35.	Major change in church activities	19
36.	Major change in social activities	18
37.	Mortgage or loan (new car, home improvement)	17
38.	Major change in sleeping habits	16
39.	Major change in number of family get-togethers	15
40.	Major change in eating habits	15
41.	Vacation	13
42.	Major holiday	12
43.	Minor violations of the law	11

Your total number of LCUs:

____

Your susceptibility to illness related to the number of stressors experienced can be assessed as follows:

Less than 150: Significantly reduced chance of getting sick in the next year

150 to 199: Suggests mild life crisis or slightly increased chance of becoming ill in the next year

200 to 299: Suggests moderate life crisis and moderately in creased chance of getting sick in the next year

Over 300: Suggests a major life crisis with greatly increased chances of becoming ill in the next year.

You may have found some of the items on the list surprising. For example, most people think holidays are full of fun and joy. However, many people feel these occasions are full of hustle and bustle, family/relationship stress, and/or financial burden and take more of a toll on a person's well-being than add to their radiance. Vacations can be stressful for some people for many reasons, including planning major details, unrealistic expectations, or being with people who take more light than they give. All these life events can make your radiance dwindle. It is what you do to recharge yourself that makes the difference.

No Free Refills

You can't reach or maintain a radiant, rich, and energetic life without conscious assessment and effort. You must intentionally identify and participate in activities that will help to continually restore you – more so when you are subjected to unusually high levels of stress. It is the intentionality and commitment to your self-care – your *soul* care – that ensures a radiant life, regardless of your current circumstances. As you pour in the positive benefit of self-care activities, you balance the depletion caused by perceived stressors.

What is the positive effect of self-care? There are many. Self-care activities can restore you when you experience intense stressors while also serving as preventive measures when you know you need to keep your pot intact and full during tumultuous times. Certain aspects of your habits, lifestyle, and environment can make you more or less vulnerable to the negative effects of stress. Researchers Miller and Smith offered a self-assessment that illustrates the positive impact of engaging in frequent self-care activities to prevent physical illness. In essence, you can effectively counterbalance the negative impact of stressful circumstances with the positive impact of intentional behaviors you have specifically identified as activities that preserve and enhance self- and soul-care. If your level of positive impact from soul-care activities exceeds the negative impact of the leakage or release, then you not only maintain a manageable or even healthy level of radiance, but you also stabilize future detrimental effects.

Take some time to complete the survey below to determine your vulnerability to illness according to the stress you currently experience.

Vulnerability to Stress Scale

Score each item from 1 (almost always) to 5 (never) as it applies to you.

__1__ 1. I eat at least one hot, nutritious meal a day.

__1__ 2. I get seven to eight hours of sleep at least four nights a week.

__3__ 3. I am affectionate with others regularly.

__5__ 4. I have at least one relative who lives within 50 miles on whom I can rely.

__1__ 5. I exercise to the point of sweating at least twice a week.

__1__ 6. I smoke fewer than ten cigarettes a day. (Score 0 if you don't smoke.)

__1__ 7. I drink fewer than five alcoholic drinks a week. (Score 0 if you don't drink alcohol.)

__1__ 8. I am about the proper weight for my height and age.

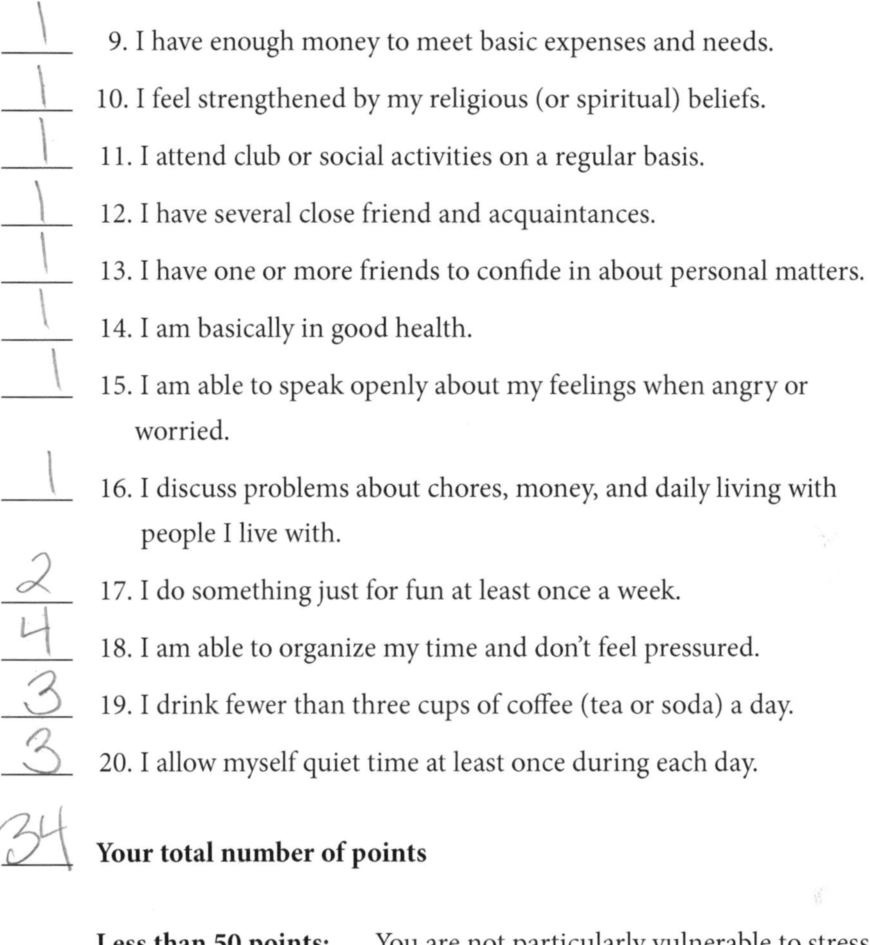

1 9. I have enough money to meet basic expenses and needs.

1 10. I feel strengthened by my religious (or spiritual) beliefs.

1 11. I attend club or social activities on a regular basis.

1 12. I have several close friend and acquaintances.

1 13. I have one or more friends to confide in about personal matters.

1 14. I am basically in good health.

1 15. I am able to speak openly about my feelings when angry or worried.

1 16. I discuss problems about chores, money, and daily living with people I live with.

2 17. I do something just for fun at least once a week.

4 18. I am able to organize my time and don't feel pressured.

3 19. I drink fewer than three cups of coffee (tea or soda) a day.

3 20. I allow myself quiet time at least once during each day.

34 **Your total number of points**

Less than 50 points:	You are not particularly vulnerable to stress.
50-80 points:	Moderate vulnerability to stress.
Over 80 points:	High vulnerability to stress.

As you can see, the amount of radiance you maintain is directly associated with the type and frequency of activities you include in your ongoing self- and soul-care plan. At one extremely stressful point in graduate school, I took the Holmes-Rahe scale to estimate the amount of stress I was under compared to the amount of self-care I was doing to balance my life at the time. My score was over 550 points! However, due to the fact I had already identified and participated in several of the ingredients to my own *Recipe for Radiance*, my risk of becoming ill (according to the Vulnerability to Stress Scale) was minimal (score of 38 on the survey above). To me, this was proof that a proactive approach to wellness was the key to leading a satisfying and joy-filled life. There is no doubt that your joy and happiness is related to the relationship between the amount of energy you expend because of your everyday stress and the amount of energy you replace by engaging in your self- and soul-care activities.

Author Anthon St. Maarten says, "There is absolutely no worse death curse than the humdrum daily existence of the living dead." In other words, you can simply choose to exist in the midst of the inherent depletion of the human condition, or you can take action to live more fully regardless of your circumstances. Radiant living doesn't happen accidentally – it takes intention and effort to create your most optimal life.

The Trap of Sainthood: Defining Selfish vs. For Self

"No more martyring myself."

~ Sharon E. Rainey

Women in particular feel they are selfish if they choose to take care of themselves. This is a multi-generational theme that has done more harm than good. Whether male or female, we always feel better – healthier and more empowered – when we take time to care for ourselves. The difference is that men have been taught to do it for their own sake, while women have been taught their self-care activities should benefit others.

For instance, women spend billions of dollars each year on beauty products and services and then spend thousands of hours to use or apply them – mostly so they look good for others. Men, on the other hand, spend their time and money on activities that will benefit them directly like golf outings, attending sports events, and purchasing big screen TVs. Culturally speaking, women have always been the primary caregivers for all family members, even if they work outside the home. Although recent years have seen more men taking part in shared household responsibilities, in general, women still spend more time (and energy) taking care of these activities.

Whether it's in a psychotherapy session, a class, or a workshop, I often encourage people to examine the distinction between selfish, selfless, and for self. When asked, most people describe selfish individuals as "self-centered, arrogant, controlling, demanding, out for themselves, insensitive, harsh, and inconsiderate," while they describe those who are selfless as "exhausted, frustrated, codependent, resentful, unassertive, and unhappy pushovers." As I outline the characteristics of each, a light bulb almost immediately goes on and the difference between the two terms is clearly understood. My next task becomes to educate participants about how to make the distinctive characteristics of selfish vs. selfless meet somewhere in the middle.

I then introduce the concept of "for self" – deciding how to give when it feels right, but also learning to set appropriate and self-sustaining limits when necessary. Understanding this balance removes the trap of sainthood and opens people to lifelong soul-care while paving the way toward radiant living.

Mother Teresa offers the ultimate image and mission of a saint – giving all she had to give and living her own life for the sake of the poor. What most people don't know is that she exhausted herself to the point of hospitalization several times in her life. She was a determined woman who helped many, but at a significant and ongoing personal cost. Was she a beautiful example of a woman with unlimited dedication to serve others? Yes. Was she a good role model for modern living? The only answer to this question is a resounding "No."

Soul Health and the Recipe for Radiance

"To know your soul is to know true health.
Only then can you reach radiant living."

~ Dr. Katherine T. Kelly

As mentioned in Chapter One, the soul is at the hub of all aspects of the human condition. It is what informs you of what you need or don't need in order to lead a radiant life. The soul is the very essence of who you are, and when you listen to what it needs and act upon its requests, your soul health is guaranteed. If even one branch of your tree of life is left unbalanced, the rest of your tree can suffer. BUT, when you work to balance just one branch, all of the others will improve as well!

In my book, *Soul Health: Aligning with Spirit for Radiant Living*, I described my Soul Health Model™, which assists you in understanding your deepest experience of health, i.e. soul health, depends on your willingness and ability to balance the ten key branches of the human condition. The beauty of soul health is the more you align the branches of health to reflect the needs of your soul, your inner ally, the more radiant you feel. This is conscious evolution at its best!

The term soul health is new to many, but it describes what all of us want – complete and optimal peace and balance at the deepest possible level. The truth is, regardless of what stressors you might have in day-to-day life, you can still feel a sense of well-being as long as you are fully aligned with your innermost needs, desires, and passions. It's your soul that tells you what will meet these needs and desires. Your radiance, then, depends entirely on your willingness to explore what is creating any misalignment with your soul's needs and desires and to commit yourself to realign your life to reflect the truest essence of who you really are.

Everyone has had times in their lives when they feel depleted, unbalanced, and spent.

Yet, everyone yearns for a sense of whole health where all aspects that contribute to well-being are vibrant, stable, and strong.

So, how do you reach radiant health? By knowing yourself at the deepest level, trusting in what you feel you need (or don't need), and acting upon these wishes and desires. As you create your unique *Recipe for Radiance*, you will learn to identify soul-care strategies that fit the needs of your innermost ally. This is what makes this recipe your own personalized soul soup.

As a preliminary exercise to considering what key ingredients you need in your individual *Recipe for Radiance,* ask yourself the following questions and use your journal to explore the answers.

1) **How can I enhance my physical health?** (Increase physical fitness, improve nutrition, work to prevent or treat an illness or disease, get more sleep, attend better to general self-care.)

2) **How can I enhance my psychological health?** (Have more positive thoughts, change unhealthy behaviors, better manage my emotions/feelings, improve my self-esteem/self-image, eliminate *dis*-ease with my life.)

3) **How can I enhance my social health?** (Eliminate unhealthy relationships; create better relationships with friends, family, colleagues, and others, spend more time with my pets.)

4) **How can I enhance my interpersonal health?** (Create healthier personal/family dynamics including communication, boundaries, respect, sense of equality.)

5) **How can I enhance my intellectual/occupational health?** (Feel more mentally stimulated, increase my curiosity to learn, feel fulfilled by work or other tasks.)

6) **How can I enhance my environmental health?** (Better enjoy my surroundings, belongings, climate, increase safety, and eliminate clutter.)

7) **How can I enhance my financial health?** (Have enough, save for the future, follow a budget, spend within limits.)

8) **How can I enhance my spiritual health?** (Increase a sense of inner

peace, meaning, and purpose; practice centering or sacred rituals; increase a sense of community with self, others, and nature.)

9) **How can I enhance my sexual health?** (Enjoy sexual interactions, create intimacy and passion, establish physical and emotional safety with my partner, heal sexual wounds.) flirt ♡

10) **How can I enhance my recreational health?** (Create and enjoy time for fun, leisure, and entertainment.) invest in second property in NC

To begin exploring the key ingredients for your *Recipe for Radiance*, consider the Soul Health Model™ and list at least one soul-care activity you already use regularly or one you know would be particularly beneficial to each branch of your tree of life.

Physical: B3

Psychological: prayer

Social: be more open to friends

Interpersonal: call home more

Intellectual/Occupational: hire business manager

Environmental: get second property in nature

Financial: allow IP to expand, don't halt growth

Spiritual: church

Sexual: flirt

Recreational: hike

In identifying these activities, you may become aware that certain ones stand out for your overall self-care. Much like when I was in grad school and identified that physical activity is one of my staple ingredients to reduce stress, you might begin to recognize certain self-care efforts that more readily counterbalance the stressors in your own life. Pay particular attention to the activities you feel you should do versus the ones that actually make a positive impact in your life. We are all influenced by others, and it is essential that you identify the key ingredients specific to your own needs that nourish your soul rather than bending to the expectation of others. Remember, your *Recipe for Radiance* is your own unique blend of activities that will nourish your soul – not those of others that may, in fact, diminish your radiance if misidentified.

Becoming Your Own Soul Chef

When you go to your favorite restaurant for your favorite meal, you probably don't really consider the amount of time and effort the chef takes to create your experience. Much thought and intention goes into producing both the main menu and the daily specials. A chef has to think about everything from what ingredients are available at the time to how they are going to get them to your table in just the right way. Their goal is to satisfy your senses so you will leave feeling both nourished and full and to ensure you will want to return when you are in need of the next enriching experience.

The same effort must go into your soul-care plan for your *Recipe for Radiance*. Like a chef, you must consider many steps in the process of feeding and nourishing your soul. In the following chapters, you will explore your plan in a detailed, step-by-step way, creating and perfecting your unique recipe as you go. As you read through the following steps, the metaphor of creating your own perfect recipe will start to take shape. It will deepen your understanding of the importance of taking time to create your personalized recipe to lifelong radiance.

Below are the steps in which chefs learn to cook a prized recipe. Throughout the following pages, you will learn to create your personalized soul-care plan using a similar process. The steps to creating your *Recipe for Radiance* include:

1) Visualizing your plate

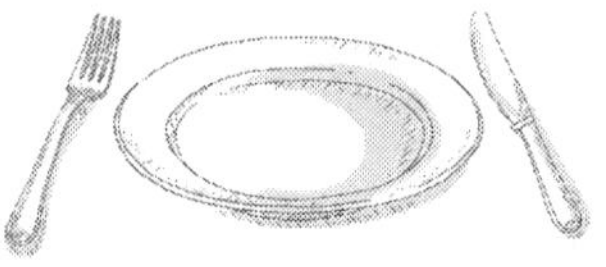

2) Developing a list of ingredients

3) Preparing the elements

4) Determining the yield

5) Defining the amounts

6) Developing the mixing and handling directions

7) Identifying necessary equipment

8) Adjusting the time and temperature

9) Testing your recipe 

10) Plating your masterpiece 

If you follow the steps listed above, you will never have to create another soul-care plan again. You will likely alter some aspects along the way, but you will forever know what it takes to both feed and restore your soul no matter what the human condition dishes out.

Throughout the following pages, you will read many examples of how I identified the ingredients for my unique *Recipe for Radiance*. Keep in mind, these are *my* essential factors in creating a more optimal life. The examples are only provided to help you understand how I came to identify each ingredient and how to identify and create your own list of key elements.

Are you ready? It's time to become your own perfect soul chef!

Chapter Three

Perfect Plate for Complete Self-Care

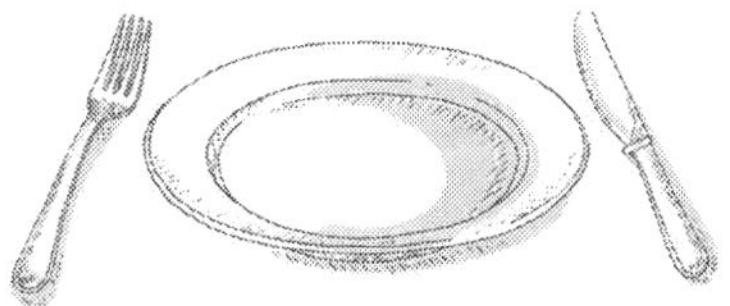

> *"Cooking is one of the strongest ceremonies for life."*
> ~ Laura Esquivel

If you were a chef, you would take time to create beautiful and nourishing meals in a very mindful and intentional manner. Chefs perfect their recipes by imagining the desired outcome or experience they would like their customers to have. They experiment with various ingredients until they come up with a combination that works. They may add a little bit of this or a little bit of that, until all the flavors, textures, and nutrients come together to please and nourish the soul, all the while imagining their intended and desired outcome as they create their perfected meal.

The same is true for creating your personalized *Recipe for Radiance*. In order to master the art of self-care, you must take your time to mindfully and intentionally imagine how your radiant life would feel. Then, you must consciously choose the soul-care behaviors (ingredients) that feed, nourish, and restore your soul. Although you likely haven't spent much time developing a structured and unique self-care plan, now is the time to master the art of soul care in order to fully assure your optimal soul health.

Your Own Soul Soup

"Slow down and take the time to really see."
~ Jeffrey Michael Thomas

Most of us remember a time when soup was the only thing that soothed our souls. Whether healing from the common cold or simply settling in for a cozy meal on a chilly night, there was nothing better than filling ourselves with a warm and nourishing substance. Remembering this sensation was how I first came up with the idea of calling your self-care your soul soup.

I can't begin to count the number of times I've asked clients or workshop participants to make a list of five things they do for self-care, fun, or leisure only to see blank stares and looks of confusion coming back at me. In most cases, they couldn't even list two self-sustaining behaviors, let alone five. After years of seeing this happen, I began using the metaphor of soul soup to teach people how to create a plan for self-care. Using the memories of how people felt when eating a bowl of warm and nourishing soup, I taught them to envision what radiance would feel like for them from the inside and out. Once they had the vision clear in their minds, I then started to teach them how to create their own list of ingredients for their own personalized soul soup so they could actually experience their imagined state of radiance on a day-to-day basis. Just like overall soul health, radiance is a constant work in progress. Once you have your recipe in mind, you always know what you need to do to either restore or nourish your soul.

In the following chapter, you will begin to explore and create the list of makings for your personalized soul soup, including your primary ingredients (the staples of your self-care), the broth (the fluid parts of your life that sustain and bind your world together), and your personalized spices (the things that flavor your life in their own unique way). Recipes have several components and these will be explored more strategically and specifically to help you make it your own.

But first, like all chefs who create amazing meals, you must take some time to envision how you want to feel as a result of having created your perfect soul soup.

Visualizing Radiance

"How we care for ourselves gives our brain messages that shape our self-worth so we must care for ourselves in every way, every day."
~ Sam Owen

Visualization Exercise

Without a clear image of what radiance would look and feel like to you, you can't create your perfect recipe for soul-care. Let's spend some time envisioning how you would like to ultimately feel once your plan is in place.

Get yourself situated in a quiet and comfortable room, free of distraction. Turn off your cell phone, dim the lights, and settle in. Sit or lie down in a position that allows you to become relaxed but remain alert and focused. Uncross your legs, arms, and/or hands as this can block the flow of your energy and your ability to think clearly. The more open your posture, the clearer the image will become.

Now take some time to simply assess how you feel as you are sitting or lying down. How do you feel both physically and emotionally? Make note of all aspects of your well-being so you have a complete idea of what parts of your life most need to be enriched. Now imagine yourself slowly becoming more radiant – full of life, more balanced, and healthy from the inside and out. Envision the process of shifting from a less enriched or radiant state to one that is vibrantly glowing.

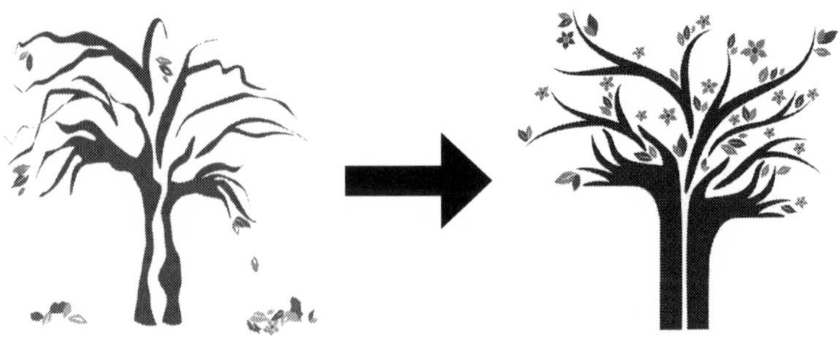

Pay attention to your reactions and responses as you make this shift. What feels different? Has your sense of physical wellness changed? How do your emotions shift? How does your outlook change? How has your energy shifted? Are you more optimistic and hopeful? Are you sensing more motivation to make positive changes in your life?

Now, take some time to fully embrace this new sense of radiance. Breathe it in…let the energy of the vision fill every cell in your body…imagine pure and radiant light emanating from you. Allow the light to extend out as far as it will, shining brightly on everything around you. Sit in this radiance while observing and absorbing everything about it. Envision this image until you can actually sense what it feels like throughout your physical body.

What does radiance feel like to you? What is different in your life? How do you feel? How have your thoughts been renewed and brightened? Have your reactions changed? How do you *know* you feel more radiant?

When you have a full vision of what radiance would look and feel like to you, create your own definition and write it down. Also, write down any other thoughts that may describe this sensation for you. Explore what you experienced as you shifted your image from less to more radiant. Perhaps you have experienced something similar before. Write about this time in your life and what you did to get there. What behaviors or healthy habits assisted you in reaching this point? If it would be helpful, take another look at the Soul Health Model™ to imagine which branches feel more vibrant than others and to think about what you've done in the past to help you to feel that way.

It is also important to acknowledge whether you had a difficult time imagining a more radiant life. Did you notice any resistance or skepticism arise during the visualization exercise? Write about this as well. It is helpful to explore and eliminate any obstacles (both from outside and from within) that may affect your willingness to create a more radiant life, all the while keeping your image of radiance very clear in your mind. Make the image more powerful than the obstacles and notice your response.

Make any further notes that might be helpful to remember on your path to radiant living.

Embracing Radiant Living

Radiance doesn't just happen on its own. As humans, we have to work at having a better life. We have to imagine what that better life would be and what actions we need to take to get there. Fitness doesn't happen without healthy eating and moderate exercise. Carefree thoughts often take time and intention to create. Living a life of love instead of fear requires a shift in perspective. And an overall radiant life doesn't just occur; we need to create it.

However, most of us think it takes far more time and energy than it actually does to create a more glowing life. We somehow think self-care is a burden, not a blessing. We put our soul-care off, all the while wishing every day we felt more satisfied and vibrant.

As you will discover in the following chapter, it is actually quite easy to start identifying your key ingredients to radiant living – once you know how to do it. The tough part is remembering to use them in the midst of experiencing your daily human condition. I admit there are times when I let my own soul soup go cold or bland, not tending to it like I should. This is normal and common in our sometimes challenging circumstances. But I'm also well aware that, if I don't take the time to prepare these ingredients and nourish my soul on a regular basis, I will wither and fail to experience my most radiant life.

Before moving on to the next chapter, make sure you have fully envisioned what radiance looks like to you. Once you acknowledge how you want to feel as a radiant being, you will already know more about how to create the path to get there.

Chapter Four

Key Ingredients for a Radiant Life

> *"When you recover or discover something that nourishes your soul and brings joy,care enough about yourself to make room for it in your life."*
>
> ~ Jean Shinoda Bolen

Identifying your list of ingredients for your personalized *Recipe for Radiance* is the single most important step in creating your optimal life. Most people can list at least a few things they like to do as part of their self-care plan, but now it is time to develop your full array of ingredients that will supply you with the ongoing nourishment you will need to both feed and rebalance your soul from this point forward.

Creating Your Soul Soup

There are three components to creating your personalized soul soup. These include:

1) **Your Primary Ingredients** (meat, potatoes, and vegetables or the staples of your soul-care plan such as physical activity, regular gatherings with friends or getting enough slept each night),

2) **Your Broth** (fluid things in life that create healthy continuity such

as lighting a candle as you prepare for your day, nightly dinners with family and daily walks with your dog),

3) **Your Spices** (things that season your life and make you who *you* are, such as wearing styles particular to your own tastes, attending events that feed your soul and decorating your surroundings to fit your unique interests).

Optimal soul-care requires the full line of ingredients, not just a few basic fixings. By taking the time to identify the key elements of your personal soul-care plan, you will be assured of leading a more nourishing and fulfilling life.

Identifying Your Primary Ingredients

"Simple ingredients prepared in a simple way – that's the best way to take your everyday cooking to a higher level."

~ Jose Andrés, a well-known chef

The primary ingredients for your *Recipe for Radiance* include the staples of what you need in order to feel balanced and whole. These are the activities that will, without fail, pull you out of a funk while also bolstering your foundation to help you get through any unforeseen stressful events that may occur. These activities may address basic needs (healthy nutrition, good sleep, security, etc.), but they are also more specific to you in balancing and restoring your life. For example, everyone needs good nutrition, but you might need a particular form of food nourishment to feel healthy. Perhaps the vegetarian diet is what really supports you, whereas your child does particularly well when consuming meat. Another example – you may rely on exercise to balance a mood, while your spouse needs quiet time by himself to achieve the same goal.

To achieve optimal soul health through your *Recipe for Radiance*, you must create your own personalized list of primary ingredients that nourish you in your own unique way. Each activity by itself might not seem distinctive, but when your key ingredients are combined, they will supply you with the staples of individualized soul-care. It is this specific blending of ingredients that will nourish the needs of your inner ally – your soul – and help you create your most radiant life. Think about a vegetable soup. Each individual ingredient of the soup – carrots, potatoes, onions, broth, and seasonings – may not seem particularly exciting by themselves, but when you combine and cook them together, you have suddenly created a delicious vegetable soup that is one of your favorite go-to comfort food recipes.

Soulful Staples

"There's only one corner of the universe you can be certain of improving, and that's your own self."

~ Aldous Huxley

As you read in A Note from the Author, I accidentally but very fortunately learned to identify the key ingredients to my own soul-care plan many years ago when I realized that physical activity was one of my go-to wonder drugs. Research is very clear that ongoing, moderate exercise is the healthiest of all self-care activities. It literally balances and maintains nearly every system within your body, including the circulatory, respiratory, endocrine, lymphatic (immune), and nervous systems – to name just a few. But honestly, I frequently get myself moving mostly because it helps to cut through the daily stress that comes with the human condition. As a result of the work I do, I tend to carry and absorb a great deal of other people's emotions, so it is imperative that I work out whenever I can in order to shed this unwanted energy. Because I can feel twitchy if I don't get a near-daily dose of this magic elixir, frequent movement has topped the list of my soulful staples for decades.

If you're like most people, you may tend to be stumped when I ask you what you do for self-care. However, there are likely lots of things you already do to feed your soul and keep yourself balanced. We just need to identify them so you can add them to your grocery list of soul-care staples. To help you explore and identify your own list of soulful staples that will go into your perfect *Recipe for Radiance*, I will spend some time naming several of my own ingredients on my primary list.

Once I identified the first one, exercise, I was able to consciously explore other key items that balanced and otherwise fed me. Now I always include these staples in my soul-care plan:

Good sleep and rest (for me that means half an hour of relaxation and then seven hours of sleep every night). I've always been a person who needed solid sleep and ample rest in order to function at an optimal level. I know people who can stay afloat with five or less hours of sleep per night, but I am not one of them. Also, I generally need at least thirty minutes each evening to simply relax, read, or decompress. I do everything within my power to make sure each of these happens on a daily basis.

Time to read (for me that means thirty minutes of time each night reading non work-related material such as cooking and travel magazines). I have always enjoyed reading, but when it comes to feeding my soul, my material of choice is usually a healthy cooking magazine or an issue of *National Geographic Traveler* or something similar. Both cooking and travel top my list for soul-care activities, so taking some time each evening to immerse myself in that kind of reading material keeps me both educated and relaxed.

Time in nature (personally, this includes time outside among trees, wildlife, etc. while walking or simply sitting on the deck). I'm a nature nut. I love being out among the trees, mountains, streams, and oceans. North Carolina has been an amazing place to live because I have the best of all worlds, including in my own backyard – literally! My home is surrounded by very tall oak, hickory, and other hardwood trees and I couldn't be happier with my chosen location. I need only to sit in my sunroom (where I am presently writing) to soak in the wonderful energy of my surroundings. In fact, this room is one of the main reasons I purchased the house – to envelop my soul with trees.

Three to five hours of spiritual activity per week (this might mean reading, inspirational movies, talks, meditation, music, etc.). To me, much of what I do holds a spiritual meaning, but I am still intentional in creating time for direct interaction with spirituality overall. Whether I read an article in a monthly periodical, watch a soulful movie, attend a spiritual conference, or hit the play button on the spiritual playlist of my iPod, I'm usually very well fed at the soul level once this key ingredient is checked off my list.

Time with dogs (For me, nightly time with my animals is a must). While I'm a self-professed nature nut, I'm also an unapologetic lover of dogs. I can spot a canine from far away and not feel my day is complete until I've given it a scratch on the head. My own dogs are more than happy to oblige my frequent need to interact. Since adopting the younger of my two pups, I've spent a lot of time at the dog park where I can get an even bigger critter fix. I've gotten to know many of the pup parents, and chatting with them feeds my soul almost as much as watching our furry babies play. Incidentally, research indicates we get a boost of serotonin, one of the happy chemicals, simply by watching an animal play. This vicarious joy deeply feeds the core of our souls.

Weekly hot salt bath (scented Epsom salts). The end of my week marks a time of closure for me as a therapist as well as the beginning of my weekend as a human being. I have always enjoyed hot baths, but when I discovered the healing qualities of Epsom salts and essential oils, I became hooked on this weekly ritual as a time to both reflect and release. Usually done on a Thursday or Friday evening, I soak in my salts, which helps to release emotional toxins so I can reset my energy for a weekend of restoration.

Frequent food preparation (cooking and baking for myself and others). It probably doesn't surprise you that one of my favorite staples of self-care is spending time in the kitchen. Food preparation never seems like a burden to me, and I intentionally reserve at least two to five hours a week for this much-loved activity. While I prefer not to cook every day, I do spend time every Sunday making something scrumptious that will carry me through part of the week. I look forward to my culinary adventures and often select themes for what I will learn to cook each year. To me, my time in the kitchen is nothing less than meditative – slicing, dicing, stirring, and kneading my way to enlightenment and my happy place and source of bliss.

Other activities have also made my staples list – time with friends, trying a new food product or restaurant, once-a-week trip to Starbucks for my decaf latte, and more. At first glance, the primary ingredients on my list may seem like little more than activities to fill my time with leisure, but these activities restore and feed my soul as well. I am well aware that, if I don't take time to immerse myself in each of them, my tank gets very low, and my life becomes misaligned.

The main thing to remember in creating your list of primary ingredients is these are activities that will, without fail, restore your worn out soul or prevent your soul from becoming worn out in the first place. As you can see from my list, your self-care activities don't have to be elaborate or pricey to be effective. Instead, they help you to reach a heightened level of radiance in a simple and functional way. These are the kinds of activities that can pull you out of the deepest of funks or keep you afloat during the most challenging events that the human condition can impose upon you.

Your Primary Ingredients

Take time to think about what restores you when you feel the worst. At least some of those activities are likely to be the primary ingredients for your *Recipe for Radiance*. Identify what takes the edge off when you're feeling the most stressed as well as what fills you up when you're most depleted. Consider whether these actions are staples in your soul health diet.

Now, list *at least* five key ingredients that always serve to realign your life and feed your soul:

1) ______________________________

2) ______________________________

3) ______________________________

4) ______________________________

5) ______________________________

6) ______________________________

7) ______________________________

8) ______________________________

9) ______________________________

10) ______________________________

Just like all master chefs, you may have to experiment with your ingredient list to make sure it reflects your perfect *Recipe for Radiance*. This process can take a while, so be patient and take care to identify the basic elements that make up your own perfect dish of life.

The Broth

Now that you have identified the staples in your *Recipe for Radiance*, take some time to explore the more fluid parts of life that help to support your personalized soul soup. These are the elements that help to keep your life simmering and assist in blending your key ingredients. For example, perhaps music is a big part of your life – something that helps to lessen your stress and rebalance your soul regardless of what is occurring. By intentionally adding a hearty helping of music to each day, you might notice an ongoing sense of peace that doesn't occur without this element.

Personally, my ongoing leisure activities usually define my broth. For instance, learning new things has always been an important part of my life. This may come in the form of traveling to new places, reading something that interests me, or watching a documentary about a curious topic. The intentional act of learning something new brings many of the other elements of my life together.

Give some thought to the activities that help to balance your life on a regular basis. Remember these activities aren't necessarily as measurable as your staples (duration, frequency, etc.), but without these ingredients, your life wouldn't feel as blended or fluid.

Here are some of the activities that create the broth for me:

Learning something new (reading about travel destinations, a new craft or home improvement project, scientific discoveries, etc.). I'm a serial learner. I am constantly picking a new topic, learning more about it, and then moving on to the next. Currently, I'm spending time learning about the therapeutic benefit of essential oils. As a result, I created my own line of oils called *Soul Health Essentials* (www.soulhealthessentials.com) to help people in their personal growth and soul development. I realized that my Soul Health Model™ lends itself to matching oils to each branch of the tree, as well as to creating blends that will help a person feel more grounded, focused, and centered. I greatly enjoy learning about the oils themselves and find myself pondering new combinations to meet the needs of client issues as they arise.

Doing something creative (cooking/baking, decorating, planning workshops, etc.). Creativity is an amazing soother of the soul. When we allow ourselves to dive into a new project, it provides inspiration and motivation for more creative endeavors. Whether trying a new recipe, planting a new garden, or painting and decorating a room, this process always leaves me feeling satisfied and relaxed.

Making things pretty (gardening, painting, cleaning). Aesthetics are an important part of my life. When I add some unique and beautiful touches to something around me, the benefits are ongoing. I add color, texture, and scents to enhance my surroundings and actively look for ways to put soulful and soothing energy into every room.

Watching a good movie (mindless entertainment). Because good movies come and go, I consider this to be part of my soul soup's broth. Often I play a movie rerun or Broadway musical soundtrack while I am cleaning, which adds a special touch to a somewhat monotonous task. This way I can relive the experience of watching or listening to the movie the first time while also getting some necessary tidying done.

Planning my next trip (ongoing process). I always have some sort of trip on the calendar. While travel itself is a staple, the planning process is a very fluid part of my life. I think often about traveling to the next desirable destination, which allows me to constantly bathe in the idea of how the trip will go. This is another recipe item that just keeps on giving, whether I ever go on the trip or not.

Listening to background music (guitar or piano music, with no words). While I do enjoy a great deal of silence, I also appreciate the melodic flow of instrumental music. Often you will find piano or guitar music playing in my car or home instead of current hits. To me, there is something wonderful about how this type of music can create a more soulful experience of life.

Journal writing (exploration and reflection about life). I have written in a journal for as long as I can remember. I don't feel the need to pick it up every day, but when I'm working through something in particular, it becomes one of my dearest friends and most effective outlets. I choose to write in a spiral notebook rather than a pretty journal because, at the end of every year, I review the pages and burn them – leaving any issues behind as I start a new year and a new chapter in my life.

Consider the more fluid activities in your life – things that come and go and help to nourish and sustain you along the way. What seems to bind your life together? What do you add to your day-to-day life to enhance your overall experience? What has been missing lately?

Now list *at least* five activities that define your personal broth:

1) ______________________________

2) ______________________________

3) ______________________________

4) ______________________________

5) ______________________________

6) ______________________________

7) ______________________________

8) ______________________________

9) ______________________________

10) ______________________________

Your personal soul soup will change over time. However, what won't change is how your life will feel more enriched and complete but when you identify the key elements that help make your life more fluid and full.

The Spices

What seasons your life? Which spices (unique flavorings) make you who you are? The spices of life in your *Recipe for Radiance* include the activities that tend to set you apart from others. These are the activities and interests that help to more specifically define who you are. For example, I love to attend modern dance performances and musicals – the more creative and quirky the better! I love things that are whimsical, different, and even a bit shocking or curious. I enjoy decorating my home with large gemstones such as amethyst, geodes, and selenite as well as unique pieces of petrified wood. I like buying fun and funky shoes that few others would dare to wear. My closest friends know I love just about any animal that exists, so I try to make a point to slow down and observe any creature that crosses my path. All of these elements of my soul soup help to season my life in a unique and fulfilling way. These are the particular ingredients that both color and flavor my world and make me the one-of-a-kind individual I am. Without these spices, my life wouldn't reflect the true essence of my soul.

Your own personal seasonings are another part of what feeds your inner ally. Without adding these crucial ingredients to your life, you would have a rather bland pot of soul soup. Instead, your personal interests add flavor to your overall well-being and feed you at the deepest level.

Here are some additional spices that season my life and may help you discover what spices up your life:

Growing herbs on the back deck. Every year since moving into my current home, I have planted herbs and tomatoes on my back deck. Since my home is surrounded by trees, this is the only place that offers enough sun for these plants to grow, a perfect location just outside my kitchen door.

Attending the occasional popular artist concert. The more unconventional the better. And the older and more seasoned the performer, the quicker I am to purchase a ticket. From Lady Gaga to Springsteen to Cher to James Taylor, I'm in the audience, happily feeding my soul.

Traveling to a local orchard to pick fruit or purchase fresh produce. There's nothing like hanging from a rickety ladder in hot weather. After I discovered there was a cherry orchard just an hour away, I joined the hundreds of others who come from all over the region just one weekend a year to pick sour cherries, the best type of cherries for baking pies. A little crazy? Yes. A lot fun? Oh yeah!

Hiking alone in the woods. Along with being a dog lover, I'm also an unapologetic tree hugger. When I get out into the woods, particularly by myself, I'm one happy woman! I've travelled the country to access many incredible forests and have enjoyed numerous unforgettable hikes in the woods – just my soul and me. The more alone I am in nature, the better fed I seem to be. There is something completely nourishing about being in the middle of a thick forest of trees. After I return from a woodsy outing, I'm already soon craving the next visit.

Collecting fortune cookie fortunes. I don't really know why, but ever since graduate school, I've saved every fortune I've ever received from a cookie. I don't eat Chinese food often, but when I do, I hold onto the message tucked inside those tasty treats. Occasionally, I'll take the jar down off of my fridge and randomly read the fortunes just to see what message I'm supposed to read that day. They often bring inspiration as I ponder where I was when I received that particular message.

Throwing theme parties. I don't have time to throw parties often, but when I do, you can bet it will be a themed gathering. Whether World UFO Day, a tropical Christmas party, or some other whimsical event, my home becomes a hub of festive activity. I go all out decorating, making fun food, and looking up interesting facts about the history of the occasion. Everyone leaves feeling refreshed and ready to return to their corner of the human condition, and I've had a ball making the whole thing happen.

Wearing unusual colors of toenail polish. As a psychologist, I can't get away with too many wild and crazy outfits. So, my toes do the talking through the various shades of turquoise blue, burnt umber orange, and Divinely Deranged deep purple tones I love to wear. I always get compliments… and often a few side glances and double takes.

Explore what seasons your life in such a way that it reflects the unique nature of who you are. What activities do people talk about when describing you to others? These are frequently the spices that are generally unique to your particular blend and that help to create your individual flavor of life.

Now, list *at least* five activities that define your spices and combine them to create your own unique *Recipe for Radiance*:

1) ______________________________

2) ______________________________

3) ______________________________

4) ______________________________

5) ______________________________

6) ______________________________

7) ______________________________

8) ______________________________

9) ______________________________

10) ______________________________

Combine these ingredients together to create your own *Recipe for Radiance*:

People assume their palate will remain entirely the same throughout their lives. In reality, as we evolve, so does our need for soul-care. As our life circumstances shift, it is likely we will have to adjust our perfect soul soup ingredients in order to better match our new interests and capabilities. However, in most cases, the main elements remain the same. For now, just spend some time exploring:

1) Your top ingredients or key elements (no-fail activities that reset your soul when you need it),
2) The elements of your broth (subtle things you add to your life to bring it all together), and
3) The spices (components unique to you that help flavor your day-to-day experiences).

It is best to explore and identify your ingredients rather thoroughly before moving on to the next chapter, so take the time you need.

Now that you have identified the ingredients for your *Recipe for Radiance*, your self-care plan is about eighty percent complete. Future chapters will help you to perfect your recipe so you know how to put it all together to create your most radiant life.

Chapter Five
Essential Preparation for Optimal Living

"The good life is a process, not a state of being. It is a direction, not a destination."

~ Carl Rogers

Perfecting Your "Recipe for Radiance"

Once your key ingredients to your *Recipe for Radiance* have been identified, you will need to perfect your soul care plan to include specific "measurements", necessary "equipment", "instructions", "time and frequency" and so on. Never before have you been so clear about what you need in order to feel more radiant, and never again will you be unequipped to balance and restore your life.

As Carl Rogers said, having a good life is a process, not a state of being. Radiance does not just appear, we must "prepare", "measure", and "mix" our lives until we come up with the perfect – and ever evolving – recipe for what feeds our unique and individual souls. What "feeds" one person's soul may not nourish that of another. The rest of this book will help you prepare and use your key components in the most effective and productive way. The remaining chapters will also help you become more proactive in your soul-care plan so you always have your recipe at hand whenever you need a boost or to recover from the inevitable stress that comes with the human condition.

Prepare the "Elements"

If you fail to plan, you are planning to fail.
~ Benjamin Franklin

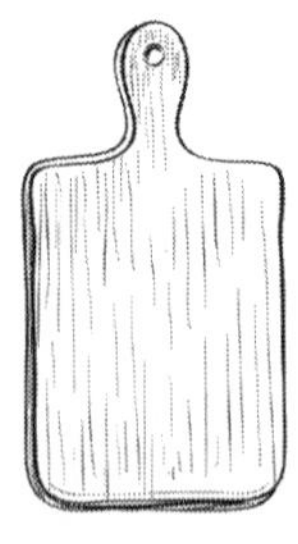

While identifying your list of ingredients is the most important part of creating your "recipe", planning ahead or "preparing" to take action is the key to success in creating a more radiant life. While most people claim they don't have time for self-care, it is often more the case they don't take the time to plan for it. It is much easier to blame our imbalance on a lack of time than it is to admit we haven't invested enough in ourselves to actually feel better. With the constant commotion of daily life, it is imperative to spend at least a little time preparing for how we will care for ourselves along the way. Otherwise, our "radiance" will fall flat and our life will become dim.

Without preparation, no meal would be made. Chefs plan their meals according to the time they have available to prepare them. They also enlist others – sous chefs and other assistants – to aid in their preparation, both to optimize their time and to ensure that all components of their well-designed meal get included. As they become more experienced in preparing meals, they learn to employ time-saving tactics, organizing both their time and elements to meet demands, while also anticipating obstacles that might get in the way. Seasoned chefs always seem to pull off amazing meals that satisfy their customers, regardless of any glitches they may run into along the way.

To become your own soul chef, you must take time to prepare all of the ingredients so these elements are ready when you need them. You must also practice your methods in order to become as experienced as the chefs in your favorite restaurant. Soul-care takes preparation and practice and without these your *Recipe for Radiance* will not fully nourish you.

Soul Food Prep

Once chefs gather their ingredients, they must prep them for use in their meals. By identifying your essential ingredients, you have already "gathered" them for use in your soul-care plan. In order to use them effectively, you must prepare them for use.

How do you do this with the ingredients for your personalized *Recipe for Radiance*? First, you must take a brief moment to explore each ingredient you identified and consider what needs to happen to have easy access to this element and to feel prepared to utilize the ingredient with minimal effort.

For example, in the introduction this book, I told the story about how I realized physical activity would forever be a "staple" in my own soul-care plan. But as you are aware, getting frequent exercise can be a challenge. Therefore, I have spent considerable time exploring ways to make sure I work this key ingredient into my busy life. First, I explored the types of exercise I enjoy, the times of day that are the most realistic for me, the places I prefer to work out, the types of clothing that are most comfortable, the brand of shoes that fits my feet the best, and even the type and size of water bottle I need according to the exercise I am choosing to do at any given time. Another thing I considered was what obstacles might get in the way of me actually hitting the gym or track. The best decision or "prep work" I did for this ingredient was to purchase an entire second gym bag, complete with all duplicated items of what I might need, so I could have it in my car at all times. This way, I had no excuses to avoid exercising after work and I was always prepared no matter what. I took the time to "prep" for ongoing and frequent exercise in a few short steps.

Another way I "prep" for physical activity is to make sure my gym clothes are ready at the beginning of each week. I know when I get home from work, there is a short window before I will become unmotivated. With this awareness, I literally walk into the house, let the dogs out and go change into my exercise clothes before I allow myself to sit down. I'm well aware that if I sit down or get distracted the moment of motivation may pass. I get my dog walk done before anything else so I can check it off the list and settle in for the rest of the evening.

Obviously, preparing to exercise takes a bit of thought, but once examined or "prepped", I never have to think about this again. The initial time spent exploring and preparing my key elements – whatever they may be – was well invested since they have all become steady parts of my everyday life.

Whether it be time to read (shutting off the television at least 30 minutes before bed at night), getting my nature fix (going for walks or sitting on my deck amongst the trees), doing something spiritual (reserving spiritual documentaries and movies ahead of time, subscribing to inspirational magazines, or downloading a well-known spiritual podcast), or taking my salt baths (keeping a clean bathtub and having salts on hand), it usually only takes a few minutes to "prep" our world to make use of the primary ingredients on our list. Without the prep, these items would just be items. Once we take it to the next step of "preparing" each ingredient – prepping whatever we need to in order to make these items or activities accessible to us – we are more than eighty percent closer to our desired state of being.

Spend some time thinking about what prep work you might need to do for each of your primary ingredients ("staples" or key elements that help to restore you), the items that make up your "broth" (fluid parts that bind your experience of life), and the "spices" (unique activities that reflect your interests and "season" your life to make you *you*). How can you prepare these ingredients ahead of time for easy use when your resources feel very low? Do you need to enlist the help of others to make sure access to these key ingredients is readily available (i.e., having someone on standby to take care of children or animals when you need to execute an item on your soul-care plan)? Do you need to "plan for planning" – or set aside time in the future to assess your life and plan for the next chapter?

Now, make a list of all ingredients on your *Recipe for Radiance* list, leaving room underneath each item. List three or more ways you can prepare to execute each item, making sure you are specific and clear. Try to include all small steps in addition to steps that seem much larger.

Also, consider how you will remember to utilize your newly identified "ingredients" in times of stress and depletion. Remembering to make use of the items on your list is just one way to prepare your elements. Place your "recipe card" somewhere handy to remind yourself of these essential ingredients to your optimal soul health.

Chapter Six

Top Yield of Soul-Care Activities

Nutrition Facts

Serving Size 1 cup (300g)
Servings Per Container 6

Amount Per Serving	
Calories 358	**Calories from Fat 90**
	% Daily Value
Total Fat 5%	15 %
Saturated Fat 1.7%	25 %
Trans Fat 1%	5 %
Cholesterol 50mg	29%
Sodium 300mg	17%
Total Carbohydrate 10g	11%
Dietary Fiber 2g	5 %
Sugars 3g	
Protein 10%	
Vitamin A 1%	**Vitamin C 3%**
Calcium 3%	Iron 1%

*Percent Daily Values are based on a 2,000 calorie diet. Your daily values may be higher or lower depending on your calorie needs.

> *"I do not know anyone who has got to the top without hard work. That is the recipe."*
>
> ~ Margaret Thatcher

Not all soul-care ingredients are created equal – they each hold their own "nutritional value" and have a different impact on us depending on how they feed our individual souls. With a true recipe, some ingredients act as the "carrier" of flavor and require large quantities despite the fact the ingredient itself offers little or none. For instance, while eating a cookie we don't think about the main ingredient – flour – as the item bringing us joy. It is the chocolate chip, sugar frosting, or raisin that defines the cookie and offers the most satisfaction. In this way, a little bit of something can go a long way, while a lot of something may leave no lasting impact.

Therefore, it is important to give some thought to which of your ingredients are most vital to your overall soul health and which ones you might need only at particular times. This chapter will help you to consider the "nutrients" each of your ingredients hold so you can prioritize them according to what you need at any particular time.

Feeding the Soul, Not the Body

A chef always has to consider whether or not their meals are going to reach the highest of expectations, leaving their customers feeling full and nourished. No one can deny how good they feel after a fully satisfying dining experience.

You leave the table feeling satiated not only physically but overall. Both your body and soul have been well fed. When asked, most people can describe the meal in detail, making note of exactly what it was that made them so satisfied, whether it be the star ingredient, the way a particular item was prepared, the combination of items on the plate, or perhaps even the specific flavors enjoyed. They describe the experience in physical, emotional, and soulful terms, which displays their deep gratification. A chef has to make sure the ingredients they choose and assemble will provide optimal satisfaction for every meal they serve.

When you think about the ingredients to your *Recipe for Radiance*, the yield of every ingredient counts. Your path to radiance depends greatly on the return provided by each item on your list. For me, when stress is high, physical activity often yields the most positive outcome. If I'm feeling extremely tired and drained, I likely opt for the hot salt bath as my magic elixir. When I have too much on my mind, I may turn to my journal to shed the static of the human condition to best ease my soul.

You see, it is not only important to identify which key ingredients make a difference in your level of radiance, it is also essential to recognize how each one nourishes you in a particular way. Just as a chef understands how each item in their meal influences the others, you must take the time to know how the elements in your own *Recipe for Radiance* blend to nourish you.

When a chef prepares a meal, they think about everything that might impact your experience and how this may occur. They choose the "star" ingredient –

the one that will become the focal point of your experience, they then build the rest of the meal around this particular item. All of the reality television cooking shows do this as part of entertaining their viewers. Producers offer an array of food items – sometimes odd, then challenge the competitors to create a meal that will provide the best dish. The final products are judged based on the chef who created the best overall dining experience. The winner's meal "yielded" the best quality plate – an experience that pleased the judges, not only in taste but level of satisfaction as well. Plates not making the cut are thrown in the trash and quickly forgotten. The high yield dishes are rarely overlooked.

High Yield Radiance

Chefs strive to choose only the best ingredients for their meals – the ones that will "yield" the biggest impact on a customer's experience. Their pantry is filled with high-quality ingredients, not the ones found in the "week old" pile. However, they do know which items need to be the best of the best and which ones don't really make a difference in the quality of the overall meal.

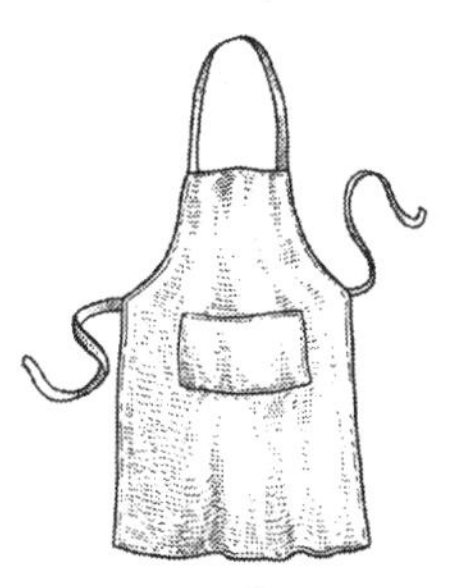

For instance, chefs who prepare meat want the best cuts and level of freshness, knowing quality and level of nutrition change with older products. Produce must be freshly picked and dairy items must be recently produced – both for taste and ability to create a desired outcome. Chefs know some herbs and spices can be stored for a while, and understand which ones must be fresh to offer the best taste. For many, the type and freshness of oil and butter makes a difference, while for others it is the type of salt that wins the show.

Pastry chefs have a different focus – they want the best types of flour, butter and yeast. They know optimal sweetness is achieved with certain kinds and combinations of fruits. Nuts are chosen depending on their ability to add crunch and depth to their delicious treats. Flavors and spices are used only with a specific outcome in mind.

Pumpkinless Pound Cake

In order to create your own "high yield" *Recipe for Radiance*, you must consider which items will yield the best possible outcome. This is done not only in the initial choice of your key ingredients but also understanding the impact each one has on you along the way. In an actual recipe, you always know when a key ingredient is missing or not effective in making a meal a good one. Unfortunately, I have a personal example of how obvious this reality is.

My friends know me as the baker in the group. I love making decadent desserts with unique combinations and flavors. One Thanksgiving, I found a recipe for pumpkin pound cake with a chocolate ganache filling I wanted to try.

I told the host about it and she said it sounded delicious and to bring it along. While checking on the cake in the oven, I noticed it was done baking earlier than the recipe had suggested. I didn't really think much about it since my oven tends to run a bit hotter than others. I cooled and glazed the cake, transported it to the gathering and proceeded to enjoy a wonderful meal with close friends. When it came time for dessert, I warned the group it seemed a little dryer than what I thought it should. All commented the flavor was nice – aromatic from all of the fall spices, but that something was "off". Everyone "semi" enjoyed the dessert but it clearly was not the usual reception I had when presenting my typical sweet creations. Something was missing and no one was fully satisfied.

When I got home and walked into my kitchen, there it was! The unopened can of pumpkin sitting on the counter, pushed back a bit out of sight. No wonder the cake was dry! And no wonder it didn't satisfy the body and soul! A key ingredient was omitted and Thanksgiving dinner wasn't complete. It didn't necessarily ruin the entire experience, but I'm guessing no one left feeling entirely satisfied either.

I immediately texted my friends and we all had a good laugh about the now famous "pumpkinless pound cake". I promised to redeem myself with a full-ingredient do-over in the near future. On New Year's Day, I presented a beautifully moist and flavorful cake and all was well – including our souls.

Optimizing Your Recipe for Radiance

It is time to optimize the items identified for your *Recipe for Radiance* by determining how each can most positively impact your life. Just as a chef knows when to add a little of this or a little of that to perfect their meals, it is important to become your own soul chef in creating your optimal soul care plan. When you hone your awareness to what your soul needs, you will always come up with the perfect "meal" to nourish your inner ally.

Let's take some time to polish and refine your soul chef skills and revisit the list of ingredients you created in Chapter Four. Below, write down each ingredient you identified, leaving room to explore how you can best use these ingredients to produce the biggest yield of each one.

Beside each ingredient you identified, make note of when each of those ingredients makes the biggest impact and how you know this has happened. Perhaps you can remember a time when that particular ingredient helped you the most. Make note of what happened physically, emotionally, or in any other way to improve how you felt before and after using the ingredient. This exercise will help you to both assess the impact the item had and also when that ingredient might be best used again in the future.

For instance, as mentioned, physical activity definitely helps to rebalance me when I'm feeling a bit off, but the type of exercise I choose also makes a big difference. Sometimes I need a long walk with the dogs, while at other times I might need to go to the gym for a more intense workout. Perhaps it is a warm spring day and time to spread mulch or trim trees; this kind of physical activity feeds me in a special away – it satisfies different physical and emotional needs.

Sometimes I need particular types of spiritual activities to feed my soul more deeply, while at others I feel a brief check-in is all I need.

By giving thought to how each ingredient more specifically improves your radiance, you will more effectively make use of each one. Use a separate piece of paper if you would like to get more detailed in the descriptions.

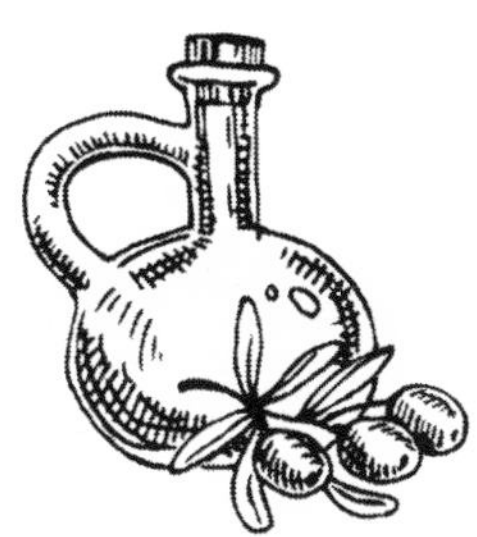

Determining the "Yield" of Your Key Ingredients

Primary Ingredients	Yield
1). ______________________	______________________
2). ______________________	______________________
3). ______________________	______________________
4). ______________________	______________________
5). ______________________	______________________
6). ______________________	______________________
7). ______________________	______________________
8). ______________________	______________________
9). ______________________	______________________
10). ______________________	______________________

"Broth" Ingredients	Yield
1). ______________________	______________________
2). ______________________	______________________
3). ______________________	______________________
4). ______________________	______________________
5). ______________________	______________________
6). ______________________	______________________

7). ______________________ ______________________

8). ______________________ ______________________

9). ______________________ ______________________

10). ______________________ ______________________

Your "Spices"	**Yield**
1). ______________________	______________________
2). ______________________	______________________
3). ______________________	______________________
4). ______________________	______________________
5). ______________________	______________________
6). ______________________	______________________
7). ______________________	______________________
8). ______________________	______________________
9). ______________________	______________________
10). ______________________	______________________

As you can see, your ultimate and perfect *Recipe for Radiance* takes time and energy to develop. Just as a chef spends the time to create a perfect meal, the investment you make now in creating your soul will nourish you the rest of your life.

Chapter Seven

Ideal Amounts for Prime Participation

"The first time you make something, follow the recipe, then figure out how to tailor it to your own tastes."

~ Ruth Reichl

The difference between being merely a good versus an award-winning chef often lies in one's ability to taste a dish and know whether everything is in balance. Star chefs can immediately assess the flavors, textures, and depth of a plate then adjust the ingredients accordingly to create the perfect meal. Although some chefs seem to have a natural talent for the art of cooking, most learn to create their prized recipes only after many imperfect attempts to get their culinary combinations just right. They must learn to create meals with finesse, a process that can take years to perfect.

The same is true for you in creating your optimal self-care plan, especially when determining just the right "amounts" of activities that will soothe and nourish your soul as time passes and your needs change.

Consider what it takes to make something as simple as gravy. Unless you buy it in a jar, you know it isn't as easy as it seems to get a recipe right. The ingredients might appear simple, but it is what each contributes when put together in the correct amount and manner that makes for a satiny smooth sauce. The key components required for making gravy are meat drippings, stock or broth, and seasonings. Simple, right? Actually, no. It often takes quite a few attempts to avoid coming up with either runny or lumpy gravy. It is all about the amount of the ingredients you use and how you blend them that makes the perfect soulful sauce.

While growing up, the standard joke in our household during holiday meals was that mom's gravy was the smoothest in the world. The truth? She got tired of fighting the battle of getting the amounts of ingredients right and eventually opted to use store-bought gravy. My mom was a good cook, but it took time to make gravy without lumps – something she didn't always have when preparing meals for a rather large family. Gravy wasn't the priority – the rest of the meal was.

Mom knew there were other dishes we all looked forward to and that sauce was just not one of them. She focused her energy on the homemade crescent rolls (a much anticipated tradition), her amazing corn casserole, and the various fruit and Jell-O salads. In our household, the stars of the show were not the main dishes (turkey, prime rib, or ham), which took very little finesse; it was everything else requiring just the right amount of "this" or "that" to make the perfect holiday meal. Mom had it figured out.

As she grew older and less able to make the full meal, we all pitched in. At that point the only missing ingredient was the love she infused in all of the food she served. We could then return the love by using her recipes to complete the meals thereafter.

The Art and Soul of Optimal Soul-Care

I must admit, I'm a bit of a "wanna be" chef. I grew up helping my mom in the kitchen, standing on a chair so I could reach the counter to help her mix batter or dough. In the fourth grade, I began 4-H cooking and cake decorating classes offered at the school, then went on to compete at the county fair, eventually winning a Reserve Champion award for my M & M cookies. Throughout the years, I realized cooking and baking were great stress relievers and creative outlets. I often found myself in the kitchen or with my head in a cookbook when I needed a break from the human condition. Now, some of my preferred leisure reading includes cooking magazines and cookbooks. Although I watch very little television, I do turn to cooking shows and competitions to entertain my brain when it is time to relax.

Over the years, I've come to realize there is both an "art" and "science" to cooking. The science part is the mechanical aspect of creating a meal identifying and collecting ingredients, knowing which utensils and baking dishes to use, and learning the basics about putting ingredients together, cooking or baking them, then serving them up. The "art" of cooking includes the creative process that allows you to do all of these tasks in a way that leaves a lasting impression once the food is consumed. This "art" also applies to the creation of your perfect soul-care plan.

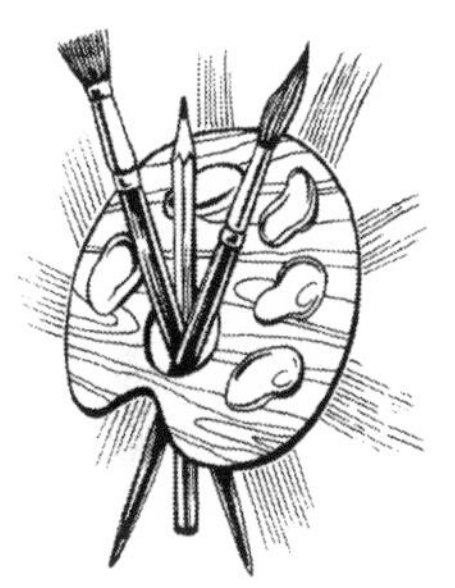

By taking the time to explore and define the "amount" needed for each ingredient you have identified for your *Recipe for Radiance*, you begin to develop the "art" of optimal self-care. When you identify the frequency and "potency" of a particular activity that is required for full nourishment, you ensure your *soul health.* For example, if you know that exercising four to five times each week at a moderate rate helps you feel charged and balanced, you are more likely to make time for this key ingredient on a regular basis.

If you do an internet search, you will find many general suggestions for self-care including things like getting a massage, taking time to read, going for a walk, spending time with friends and family. But no one knows what you *really* need more than your own soul does. If you listened to your inner ally – the essence of who you really are, you would admit these general options are not personalized enough to feed and restore you at a deep level.

Exercise: Testing your Amounts

To help you develop the art of creating your optimal recipe for radiance, I encourage you to complete the following exercise which will help you more specifically identify the right "proportions" of each ingredient on your list. By doing so, you will know what you really need in order to maintain your life, restore it, or thrive.

Revisit each item listed in your *Recipe for Radiance*. Write them down again below. In the second column, state a few things about what this item does for you when you make use of it just once. This will allow you to assess the "amount" and "potency" of each so you know how much of it you need in your day-to-day life to feel healthy.

For example:

Primary Ingredient	**"Potency"**	**"Ideal Amount"**
1) Exercise	Calming, decreases stress, fun	4-5 times/week
2) Something spiritual	"Grounding", inspires me, learn	2-5 hours/week
3) Nature "fix"	"Connects" me, shifts perspective	2-4 hours/week

As I mentioned in previous chapters, exercise provides my "sanity" – it helps me release, balance, and ground myself. Over the years, I have found if I get at least four hours of exercise a week I can remain somewhat balanced. Anything less, and I get "twitchy" with nothing feeling right and other self-care activities seeming to wane. When I get more than four hours, I feel fantastic. At the very least I am aware of the minimum amount of exercise necessary to maintain a generally balanced life.

Because I find great solace in having a spiritual practice, I actively seek ongoing activities to help feed my soul. These come in all shapes and sizes from reading some inspirational quotes to sitting down to a long meditation.

I constantly assess what and how much of "it" I need in order to maintain a connection with myself and spirit.

Nature is one of the greatest healers of all for me. The location of my home allows me to get an almost constant infusion of nature's finest energy. I still need to be outside in order to soak it all in. Whenever possible, I exercise outdoors so I can get the physical release and spiritual infusion that is provided to me by nature.

When taken alone, each of these key ingredients packs a big punch. When combined, much like combining ingredients of an actual recipe, each one boosts the potency of the others and creates the perfect combination of soul-nourishing effects.

Now, spend some time exploring the potency of each of your ingredients in your *Recipe for Radiance*, then determine and list the ideal amount of each you need integrate into your life on a regular basis.

Determining the "Amount" and "Potency" of Your Key Ingredients

Primary Ingredients	Potency"	"Ideal Amount"
1) ____________	____________	____________
2) ____________	____________	____________
3) ____________	____________	____________
4) ____________	____________	____________
5) ____________	____________	____________
6) ____________	____________	____________
7) ____________	____________	____________

8)	______	______	______
9)	______	______	______
10)	______	______	______

Broth Ingredients		**"Potency"**	**"Ideal Amount"**
1)	______	______	______
2)	______	______	______
3)	______	______	______
4)	______	______	______
5)	______	______	______
6)	______	______	______
7)	______	______	______
8)	______	______	______
9)	______	______	______
10)	______	______	______

Your "Spices"		**"Potency"**	**"Ideal Amount"**
1)	______	______	______
2)	______	______	______
3)	______	______	______
4)	______	______	______
5)	______	______	______
6)	______	______	______

7) ____________________ ____________________ ____________________

8) ____________________ ____________________ ____________________

9) ____________________ ____________________ ____________________

10) ____________________ ____________________ ____________________

Did your ideal amounts surprise you? Some items probably require less regularity than expected, while others need to be increased in frequency. In my psychotherapy practice, I can make very few guarantees. However, when working with a new client I always make a suggestion to exercise at least three times a week for two weeks. After this period, a person is pretty much guaranteed to benefit from the physical activity due to the direct positive affect exercise has on the limbic system (balances and regulates mood). With regular exercise, most people recognize not only a boost in mood, but other benefits as well. They become more motivated to make exercise a regular part of their day.

You might have been surprised to find that certain ingredients require only a "dash" here and there in your life. In some cases, a little bit does go a long way. Perhaps you need less time to spend with friends or family than you did in the past or a personal interest or hobby that once held a primary spot in your life might has faded into the background. A small dose of these ingredients might occasionally have such a strong affect that they hold you until the next time you need more of them in your life.

Adjusting the Amounts

Tastes change over time, leaving us with a shifting palate throughout our lives. Sometimes the tasty treats we once enjoyed may no longer be our favorites. Much is the same for the shifting of our soul-care needs. As we grow and evolve – and age unfortunately, our needs change. Therefore, it is important to revisit your *Recipe for Radiance* often so you can adjust the "amounts" of each ingredient.

Keep in mind that your *Recipe for Radiance* is a life-long plan for optimal self-care. The basics will likely remain the same, but the amount and frequency of these activities will likely change. Just as a recipe can be altered to save time, address changing nutritional and dietary requirements, and plan for shifting portion sizes, your self-care strategy will be adjusted to accommodate your soul's evolving needs.

The art and soul of self-care allows us to create our most radiant life… and keep it. Spend some time thinking about how you will become a more artful agent in your lifelong quest for radiance.

Chapter Eight

Mixing and Handling Instructions for Sustainable Self-Care

"No matter what the recipe, any baker can do wonders in the kitchen with some good ingredients and an upbeat attitude!"
~ Buddy Valastro

My first role in the kitchen was the "master mixer." As with most kids who find themselves in the kitchen at a young age, I was put in charge of the "mixing" station. My mother would place the ingredients in a large bowl in the kitchen sink and pull up a chair so I could stand on it to reach the work area. She pulled up my sleeves, then let me dig in – sometimes literally with my hands – to complete the task of mixing ingredients. I loved the job and took great pride in my work.

In kitchen hierarchy, I would have been considered the sous chef, literally translated as "under chef." While the chef is in charge of overall management of the kitchen, the sous chef follows closely and executes all plans and demands that are laid out. It may seem like a menial role, but in truth, it is the optimum place to be in the hierarchy if you want to learn to cook. It is also the best place to learn the chef's top skills – and even their best-kept secrets.

The greatest way to score points with the chef is when you make them look good or help to make their meals superior. On more than one occasion, I caught mistakes and omissions my mom would make while racing around the kitchen. At about age four, I realized my mother didn't add the eggs to the bowl of ingredients for meat loaf. I asked, "Aren't you going to add the eggs?" and my mom stopped, thought about it, laughed, and then went to the refrigerator to grab the carton. She told that story many times and to this day I've never forgotten to add eggs to a recipe.

The Master Mixer

Learning to mix ingredients correctly is more than a simple task. In your *Recipe for Radiance*, it is, in fact, one of the most important steps to creating an optimal life. You must know when to add certain ingredients and how to mix and handle them properly. Just as a sous chef, you can watch others to learn, but at some point, you must become your own lead cook – or soul chef – in order to execute the perfect recipe.

For instance, when a big project is due, you must anticipate what is needed to stay afloat. You must "mix" your self-care activities into your busy schedule in just the right way to remain healthy and well during the most taxing of times. During the holidays, you might need to "handle" your activities differently than when you are in your normal routine. This guarantees a better outcome of enjoying festivities without feeling drained and "malnourished" in terms of self-nurturing events.

Remembering to get to bed at a decent hour is much like remembering to add the eggs to your recipe – this may be the key ingredient that "holds" you together regardless of a crazy schedule. The key to any chef's success is to learn the nuances of mixing and handling the ingredients of any recipe to accommodate circumstances at the time of preparing meals.

With this in mind, it is important to take the time to determine and define specific methods for mixing and utilizing your ingredients. Regardless of whether you are in a normal daily routine or a busy and hectic time of the year, your ability to mix and handle your *Recipe for Radiance* determines the outcome of your soul-care plan.

In other words, you may need to "mix" some relaxation time into each day at a specific time to guarantee your "recipe" is managed on a regular basis. You may need to specifically identify ways to ways to manage disruptions in your schedule to make sure all aspects of your health are tended. Perhaps you need to schedule a massage a month ahead in order to carry out your most desired self-care plan. Whatever is required to "mix and handle" your recipe, think through the steps to making your essential "ingredients" or activities for *soul care* happen.

Mindful Mixing

Mindfulness can be defined as the "moment-to-moment awareness of the good, the bad, and the ugly" according to Jon Kabot-Zinn, the founding director of the Center for Mindfulness in Medicine, Healthcare, and Society at the University of Massachusetts. In other words, as we become and remain mindful of our circumstances, we can then create a plan for how to react and respond.

When it comes to good self-care, we must learn to respond to the ebb and flow of the human condition. We must become aware of what we need at any given time, then execute a plan to keep ourselves healthy and well. We must "mix" in healthy activities to counteract the stressful reality of day-to-day life. Mindfulness is the first step, consciousness is the second.

The difference between leading a mindful versus conscious life is this: mindfulness is about awareness, while consciousness is about what we will do with this awareness. There is much more action involved in leading a conscious life – it is taking awareness to a higher level. It is recognizing that omissions to our self-care plan now will have a direct and negative impact later. Consciousness is about anticipating what we will need in order to lead our most optimal life and doing something about it now to prevent an undesirable outcome.

Most people who struggle with self-care seem to overlook the importance and even avoid the effort it takes to execute – or mix in – healthy behaviors as stressful events occur. Many are overcome by the need for immediate gratification rather than the sustaining effect of healthy self-care. Admittedly, it does take a great deal of self-control at times to prioritize a brisk walk vs. a trip to the fridge. Both are nurturing activities, but with very different outcomes.

The key to a well-executed soul-care plan is to mix and handle the ingredients to your *Recipe for Radiance* on a regular basis, prior to the occurrence of stressful life events. This makes it easier to maintain healthy balance regardless of when life decides to turn up the temperature. In any recipe, well-mixed and handled ingredients set the stage for a lovely and balanced meal. In your *Recipe for Radiance*, the same is true in leading a scrumptious life.

Handling Instructions

A recipe would not be complete without knowing how to handle the ingredients. In creating your ideal *Recipe for Radiance*, it is imperative you develop your own handling instructions in order to create your optimal life. Remember, once you create your perfect recipe, you will never again have to consider what it will take to improve your life. You simply have to follow your already created instructions, then enjoy the benefits of your beautifully delivered soul-care plan.

A "Culinary Care" Calendar

One of the best ways to guarantee optimal self-care is to intentionally "mix" it into your week. I recommend scheduling each activity, taking care to consider the events of the upcoming week, then anticipating what activities you will most need to add to your recipe to guarantee a positive outcome.

- Consider your typical week and schedule things like physical activity, time with family and friends, time alone, and other activities that are primary ingredients or staples of your overall self-care.

- Explore how you can also add your "Broth" and "Spice" ingredients in such a way that would enhance your well-being.
- Anticipate whether particular upcoming events will be stressful and what you might need to add or "mix" to your schedule to restore you or maintain a healthy balance.
- Pay attention to what each activity or ingredient "yields" and when these activities might best be placed throughout your week.
- Look further ahead to major projects, planned events, or holidays that might upset your daily routine. Schedule activities throughout these times that will assist in maintaining your self-care.
- If you are trying to get into a routine of self-care, schedule time to plan your week's self-care. This usually takes much less time than we think. It is the mindfulness about our schedule that seems to take more effort than the time it actually requires to put a plan in place.

A well-planned *Recipe for Radiance* will guarantee success. I learned this years ago as I was preparing to leave my career as a professor at a medical school. I realized early on that the position would not only limit me in pursuing what I actually wanted to do, but also in how I could take care of myself while under the pressure to perform at an unrealistic and undesirable level. A full-time work week was considered to be a minimum of fifty-five hours. For someone who teaches healthy behaviors and self-care to others, this seemed more than a bit ironic and contradictory.

As I embarked on the adventure of starting my own private practice, I literally scheduled my self-care activities into my week, including exercise, time to air out my brain, and time to write. I have maintained most of the original plan, but had to adjust – of all things – the time I had set aside to write. I originally scheduled Fridays as my day dedicated to writing articles, books, or whichever project was due. But I quickly realized that I had to "mix" in some time to relax and clear my brain before I could effectively sit down at my computer. So, instead of Fridays becoming my days to write, I use those mostly to decompress, run errands, clean, and shift my brain from therapy to writing. I intentionally do very little on Friday evenings, opting instead to relax and release any residual stress from the week (usually through taking a hot salt bath and reading or watching a movie). What I found was my brain was fresh and ready to write on Saturday mornings. I was much more productive and effective once I "mixed and handled" my self-care ingredients to prepare for writing the next day. Even fifteen years later, I hold to this general schedule.

Writing Exercise

On some blank sheets of paper or in your self-care journal, take some time to write your responses to the following questions:

1) On a day-to-day basis, when is the best time for me to exercise? Consider which kinds of exercise are best for each day.

2) During my week, which days do I need to block out time for friends and family?

3) During my week, which days to I need to block time out for myself?

4) Explore which days tend to be the most stressful for you. What self-care activities do you need to engage in prior to these challenging days in order to enhance your week? Following these activities?

5) Which days are best to implement your primary ingredients – or staples of self-care?

6) Which days do you need to add the ingredients of your "Broth"? And how would this be best done?

7) When in your week could you add your "Spice" ingredients to assist in "flavoring" the upcoming days or events?

8) On a monthly basis, what do you need to "mix" in to ensure your optimal self-care?

9) When you look at the upcoming months, how can you "mix and handle" your soul-care activities to help you lead a more optimal life?

10) Who do you need to enlist – a sous chef – (aka, friend, partner, family member, massage therapist, psychotherapist, barista, etc.) – to help you best execute your soul-care plan?

Although your optimal self-care plan takes time and effort to create, the value is exponentially beneficial. One client taped a picture of The Soul Health Model™ onto the wall of her laundry room so she could ponder her soul-care needs as she folded towels and clothes. Another uses her time driving home from work to consider what she will need that evening and/or for the rest of the week to feel balanced and whole. Others sit down once a week or month to add self-care to their calendar to guarantee they make time for the most potent ingredients of their soul-care plan.

You see, once identified, it really doesn't take much time to decide when to "mix" in the ingredients of our *Recipe for Radiance.* A little time taken now goes a long way in creating your optimal life.

Chapter Nine

Necessary Equipment for Proper Preparation

"In department stores, so much kitchen equipment is bought indiscriminately by people who just come in for men's underwear."

~ Julia Child

All of the best chefs learn to choose and use their equipment wisely. They learn which pots, pans, and plates work best for them and for the meals they want to create. They find their favorites and tend to stick with them for the remainder of their career, only changing if a new product or gadget comes along to make their job easier or better.

While taking 4-H cooking classes in grade school, I proclaimed I wanted to be a chef when I grew up. Of course, I had no idea what that would mean at the time, but to help me figure it out my father gave me an Oster food processor and a chef's hat for Christmas. These gifts were quite unique for someone who was only in the fourth grade, but it did help me learn the ins and outs of kitchen equipment. (I also came to know that my father wanted to test his own culinary skills with the processor as well.) I learned to make various types of bread, pastries, and other tasty delights all because of that one dynamic food machine. It finally saw its last day some 25 years later.

My interest in kitchen equipment has not waned, and took an even stronger hold on me when I went out on my own. As most college and graduate students, I didn't have much extra money to spend on anything that was not a necessity. Even after landing my first job as the Director of Behavioral Science at a medical school, I still had bills and student loans to pay. Soon after taking the job, a Bed, Bath & Beyond store opened just down the road from work. This created the convenient opportunity for me to stop by and peruse the latest kitchen gadgets I could incorporate into my kitchen. As a boost during a stressful week or a reward for a completed project, I occasionally spent a few dollars to add to my culinary collection. Whether a new spatula, apple cutter, or cherry pitter, that five or ten dollars went a long way in both bringing me joy and building an inventory of kitchen equipment I could use for many years to come. Because cooking and baking is one of my main stress relievers – an activity that deeply feeds my soul – I rely on these simple instruments to create not only wonderful meals, but also a more optimal life.

The Well-Stocked Pantry

Besides needing the key ingredients for your *Recipe for Radiance*, you also need the equipment necessary to make use of your identified list of soul-care items.

- Do you have the exercise shoes and clothes you need to remain healthy and safe?
- Are your shelves "stocked" with the books or magazines you need to relax?
- Is your IPod or other device full of your favorite music?
- Do you have a notebook ready for your journal-writing needs?

Part of your self-care planning entails having the right "equipment" available at any given time so you can easily and consistently execute your soul-care plan. This can be an ongoing process as shoes wear out, new authors emerge on the scene, and new products hit the shelves. Once you identify the main ingredients to your *Recipe for Radiance*, they will generally remain about the same. Although the drawers and cabinets in my kitchen took a while to fill, the core self-care activity of cooking remained the same. Occasionally, I come across a new gadget or need to replace a spoon or spatula, but my sustained love of cooking will always be something that feeds my soul.

Although creating your ideal *Recipe for Radiance* provides the ingredients and instructions, it is also important to identify what it will take to *implement* your recipe. In other words, do you need to purchase and "stock" more music so you have your favorite tunes available? Do you need to check your bath salt supply to make certain your weekly soak in the tub occurs? What do you need to add to your shopping list to ensure you have an optimal week? Your soul-care plan is only as effective as the "equipment" you use to follow through.

Taking Inventory

The "equipment" necessary for your *Recipe for Radiance* may not include actual physical objects. Instead, the equipment might be an appointment for a massage, music for your audio player, a place to meditate, or the ability to book a vacation. According to Webster's Dictionary, the definition of "equipment" is "necessary items for a particular purpose." The equipment necessary for your *Recipe for Radiance* can include anything - material or not - that will help you to feed your soul and create a more optimal life.

Return to the lists of your Primary, Broth, and Spice ingredients you identified earlier. Take some time to decide if you have the equipment necessary to execute your soul-care plan. Keep in mind, part of feeding your soul may be to acquire some of your equipment so you don't need to have all of it before executing your strategy. Just as the occasional purchase of a new kitchen gadget feeds my soul, exploring how to more aptly stock your own self-care pantry for the items you need might be part of improving your overall health as well.

Write down ideas about the soul-care "equipment" that might make your *Recipe for Radiance* easier to apply.

Primary Ingredients	**Necessary "Equipment"**
(1) ____________________	____________________
(2) ____________________	____________________
(3) ____________________	____________________
(4) ____________________	____________________
(5) ____________________	____________________
(6) ____________________	____________________
(7) ____________________	____________________
(8) ____________________	____________________
(9) ____________________	____________________
(10) ____________________	____________________

"Broth" Ingredients	**Necessary "Equipment"**
(1) ____________________	____________________
(2) ____________________	____________________
(3) ____________________	____________________
(4) ____________________	____________________
(5) ____________________	____________________

(6) ______________________ ______________________

(7) ______________________ ______________________

(8) ______________________ ______________________

(9) ______________________ ______________________

(10) ______________________ ______________________

Your "Spices" **Necessary "Equipment"**

(1) ______________________ ______________________

(2) ______________________ ______________________

(3) ______________________ ______________________

(4) ______________________ ______________________

(5) ______________________ ______________________

(6) ______________________ ______________________

(7) ______________________ ______________________

(8) ______________________ ______________________

(9) ______________________ ______________________

(10) ______________________ ______________________

Hopefully, as you identified which "equipment" you must put in place, you also recognized what you need to do to acquire it. For instance, if you need to find a new massage therapist, you might have thought of a different place you've been meaning to try. Or perhaps you recognized you already have some of the necessary equipment, but you haven't put it to good use. Perhaps you can “repurpose” what you already possess to meet the needs of other items on your list. For example, changing a lightbulb to a softer color or amount of light can shift the entire mood set within a room. Sometimes we just have to get a little creative in determining what kind of equipment can serve the purpose to feed our soul.

Remember, you don’t need all of the gear up front to match the ingredients on your list before you get started on your soul-care plan. Radiance is a process, and as I continue to learn new ways to take care of myself, you will too. Our soul’s evolution entails growing and changing along with our self-care needs.

I suggest finding a time in your week to take at least five minutes to do an inventory of your soul-care “supplies” to ensure you have everything you need for that week. Remaining prepared is part of the battle, but this preparation allows us to make instant and easy use of the items we identified in our list for our *Recipe for Radiance.*

Chapter Ten

Time and Temperature for a Well-Baked Life

> *"All we have to decide is what to do with the time that is given us."*
> ~ J.R.R. Tolkien, The Fellowship of the Ring

People seem to believe the biggest obstacle to self-care is a lack of time. The real obstacle is our refusal to actually take the time – no matter how much or how little – to care for ourselves. We haven't "decided" we are important enough to do so, hoping our health and our soul will wait for us in the future.

Because time always seems to escape use, we tend to think of self-care as an all-or none-scenario, despite the fact that self-care becomes most crucial when we are experiencing stressful times. Either we exercise or we don't. We take the time to read – or not. We make the effort to cook ourselves a healthy meal – or skip it and order pizza. Self-care doesn't come in a one size fits all model anyway, so why not allow some flexibility in our self- or soul-care plan to accommodate inevitable shifts in our day-to-day living?

"Going with" the Times

As the Nationwide Insurance commercial says, "Life comes at you fast." Sometimes we lose sight of what is important and what will help us maintain wellbeing in the future. The human condition requires flexibility whether we like it or not and the willingness to adjust is, in fact, what makes us human.

The concept of "survival of the fittest" states that the continuance of organisms depends on their ability to adapt. The same is true for radiant living—we must constantly adjust to what is going on in our lives to maintain a certain level of satisfaction and vitality in the way we live.

If you watch reality television cooking shows, you know culinary curveballs are tossed at competitors in every show, many related to limiting the time provided to complete a given kitchen task. The chefs are forced to think on their feet to accommodate these limitations and shift their strategies accordingly. It is part of the game and part of what keeps viewers watching day after day. Somehow we like to watch others overcome a time crunch, but we don't necessarily want to wrestle with this challenge ourselves.

Becoming your own soul chef requires the willingness to fine-tune the duration and intensity of your soul-care activities to meet your needs in the moment. Some days you won't be able to exercise for a full hour. The question becomes how will you adjust your days and times to meet your minimum needs? Are you skimping on time to write in your journal? How might you shift your daily schedule to add time to sit down and write?

The Cave Man's Approach to Cooking

Exercise is not natural. That's why so many people struggle to incorporate it into their daily routine. Cave men didn't stop everything to go to the gym. Instead, they already led active lives and didn't need to drop down to do push-ups or sit-ups in the midst of their day. So, why should we expect it to be easy to get physical activity on a regular basis, especially with our inevitable hectic lives?

This is why we pre-plan our self-care activities, as emphasized in the last chapter, while adjusting these activities to fit the needs and circumstances of each day. For instance, in writing the last few chapters, I had to adjust my own physical activity and writing time to accommodate a major snow storm that moved through the area. Record snowfall shut down the city and my typical walks and trips to the gym were eliminated. My scheduled writing day became an all-day "clear the driveway" event, shoveling seventeen or more inches of snow so I could get my car up a very long path to the road. Although I got plenty of physical activity as I cleared the drive, it left me feeling like my writing time had been cut short. However, the reality of being snowed in allowed me to shift my client load to later in the week, opening up time to write two chapters in twenty-four hours. I looked at the situation, solved the immediate problem of digging my way out, all the while getting physical activity. My writing time was altered, but I still accomplished what was needed.

Flexibility is the key and chefs know that sometimes circumstances beyond their control may derail original plans for a carefully conceived meal. Just as the competitors on cooking shows have to adjust, so must we as the executive soul chefs of our own lives.

When the Soul Chef Goes on Strike

Everyone I know, including myself, rebels against their own self-care plan. The struggle to create and maintain a more optimal life is, in and of itself, a challenge unique to the human condition. We all have times when we don't want to do whatever it takes to help us feel better. We find every way possible to avoid a self-care activity, finding plenty of alternatives which generally only make our condition worse. Perhaps you've just experienced a difficult life event or undergone a major change in a relationship, work, or lifestyle. Maybe you feel stuck and uncertain of the future. The last thing we usually want to do at these times is put effort into feeling better.

It is at these times when we most need to adjust our self-care plans, not to accommodate others, but to accommodate ourselves. Sometimes our soul is as tired as our body and we just need to do the bare minimum to stay afloat. In these instances, I help people renegotiate their needs and adjust their soul-care plan to match what they have available to themselves, which at times may be very little.

For instance, I often encourage people to continue physical activity but suggest accomplishing only half of what was in their original plan. This allows them to reap the benefit of some ongoing movement and emotional release from the activity, while reserving energy as they take the time for self-restoration. If a person is accustomed to cooking on a regular basis, but doesn't have the energy to do it every night, they may want to consider taking turns with a partner or spouse or "batch" cooking so they will intentionally have leftovers to sustain them throughout the week. When a person feels guilty they aren't spending enough time with friends or loved ones, I urge them to set aside one day a week to see all of them, giving themselves permission to have some time alone on the other days.

Sometimes the "temperature" or intensity of an activity needs to be ramped down or decreased in order to accommodate current circumstances. Recently, I suffered a stress fracture in my left foot which kept me from jogging or doing any other impact exercise for several weeks. Instead of stopping everything, I adjusted my routine to use the elliptical and stair climber instead. During times of extreme stress, I often opt for silence rather than a popular radio station or CD in the background, for times when I need to decrease the intensity of auditory stimulation.

The time it takes to implement a self-care activity and the temperature – or intensity – in which you do it are all negotiable parts of your soul-care plan. While the types of activities won't likely change in your ingredient list, you might need to alter the "amount" or intensity of any given element to accommodate your current circumstances. Just as a chef adjusts a meal according to the ingredients available to them, you must adjust your self-care activities according to what your needs are at any given time.

Adjusting the Timer

Chefs are well aware that every oven performs differently and varies in consistency of temperature. When using equipment unfamiliar to them, they must constantly watch their food as it bakes or broils. The same vigilance is necessary in implementing your soul-care plan. We must stay aware of how "well" we are in order to know if we are "done", "burnt", or "undercooked." Becoming aware of what you need at any given moment will help you test your "doneness" and allow you to master the art and soul of self-care.

Think about the self-care plan you have developed while reading this book. Consider what might require adjustment to better meet the needs of your allotted self-care time, as well as the intensity—or "temperature" of each activity best meeting your needs. Spend some time considering the following questions to assist you in adjusting the "time" and "temperature" for your *Recipe for Radiance*:

- Presently, do the ingredients fit your needs in terms of time spent and "intensity" or temperature of each activity?
- What needs to be adjusted to best fit the current requirements and level of energy you have to expend on your Recipe for Radiance?
- Which ingredients might need to be increased immediately to create your most optimal health?
- Which ingredients seem less important?
- Do any activities ("ingredients") need to be decreased to better match your current level of energy?

- Can you adjust the time spent on each activity to better meet your current needs?
- Which ones need extra attention or intensity (aka "temperature")?
- What adjustments might need to be made to accommodate upcoming events or changes?

Chapter Eleven

Taste-Test for Soul Health Success

"Once you have mastered a technique, you hardly need look at a recipe again and can take off on your own."
~ Julia Child

Most serious chefs strive to earn the recognition and respect of not only the people they serve, but also their many peers in the restaurant world. Receiving an award of a "Michelin Star", the benchmark of gourmet dining is the highest honor a restaurant can receive and can be considered something similar to receiving an Oscar award in the culinary world. French in origin, the Michelin *Red Guide* started as a guidebook for travelers in Europe, offering suggestions for the best food, gas stations, and hotels along the way. Currently, the guide covers three cities in the United States as well – New York, Chicago, and San Francisco. In order to receive much sought after accolades for their cuisine, restaurant chefs are recognized as "rising stars", showing great potential to make their way up the hierarchy of possible number of awarded stars. Any chef who is in the running for a star is sure to be extremely vigilant about the quality of food and service they provide. The most stars a chef and restaurant can earn are three, a number they work very hard to maintain once they achieve this level of culinary excellence.

Similarly, creating your *Recipe for Radiance* requires both a heightened level of attentiveness as your own personal soul chef and attention to your own needs as opposed to those of others. Much like the dedication of a Michelin Star chef, you must also commit to ongoing excellence in self-care in order to maintain an optimal life.

Good chefs always experiment, "taste", and perfect their recipes with intention and dedication while refining their meals. It not only takes time to identify the right ingredients for your *Recipe for Radiance*, it also takes knowing how to test your recipe to see if it provides the intended outcome while envisioning your perfect recipe prior to getting started. This chapter will help you take an initial look at your self-care recipe to help you test whether you are achieving the desired results.

Are You "Done" Yet?

Kicking old and starting new habits isn't easy. That's why most people fail at goals and New Year's resolutions so quickly. For this reason, you can expect to make ongoing adjustments to your *Recipe for Radiance*, for… well, probably for the rest of your life! Remember, optimal health is a process, not a destination and as the human condition ebbs and flows, so will your optimal soul-care plan.

Back in graduate school, I decided to eliminate soda from my daily consumption of beverages. At the time, I was a diet, caffeine-free Dr. Pepper junkie. I couldn't drink anything with caffeine because it contributed to my migraines and I didn't want the extra calories from sugar, so I went for the artificially sweetened version. Eventually, I realized I was paying a lot of money for a liquid offering no nutritional value, so I decided to change to water. Believe it or not, this process took almost two years to achieve.

First, I had to work on eliminating a much desired treat from my daily routine. My pattern was to drink a few cans a day, starting early in the morning. Not only did I have to work my way out of one habit, I also had to work my way into a new one.

Strangely enough, I had to "test" how I was going to drink water for over a year to figure out my preferences. In the process of switching beverages, I realized I prefer to drink water out of a plastic tumbler. I also learned I prefer my water to be room temperature instead of super cold or warm because my teeth are sensitive, perhaps as a result of braces worn as a teen. I also recognized I drink more water in restaurants when accompanied by lemon or lime, therefore, I always ask for some. Having learned all of this, I now fill a 72 oz. pitcher of water and bring it to work. This gives me the correct amount for daily consumption and I do not need to give it any more thought. After I learned all of this – or was "done" baking in that way – I could move on to reviewing the next health behavior.

You may have heard it takes three weeks for a new habit to form. Unfortunately, this is not what the research shows. It was simply an observation made by a plastic surgeon who thought this was about the amount of time patients took to adjust to their new appearance. In reality, research shows it can take anywhere from 18 to 254 days for a habit to form, depending on the behavior and complexity of the change. While this might seem like a long time, it does confirm change can be difficult and no one should expect to completely modify his or her life in a few short months. The beauty of this is you can continue honing your skills as you learn to master the art and soul of self-care.

As you embark on your self-care journey you can expect it will take time to perfect your personal *Recipe for Radiance*. Consider the following estimated time-frames for shifting a new behavior into a habit:

- Simple behavior (such as setting out your daily vitamins): Two weeks to a few months
- Semi-complex behavior (such as remembering to actually take your daily vitamins): A few months up to a several months
- Complex behavior (such as making a morning smoothie to naturally receive minerals and vitamins—eliminate need for daily vitamins): Several months to a several years.

Sharing these estimates of behavior change is meant to normalize the fact it will take time for change to occur. It will also take time to create and maintain the most effective *Recipe for Radiance* for your ultimate self-care. Most people avoid creating a self-care plan because 1) they don't know where to start, 2) they don't take the time to explore their needs and decide what self-care activities will fulfill these needs, and 3) they think they will fail, so they aren't inclined to even get started.

The truth is, health is a process and optimal living is something at which we have to work. However, the payoff when we slowly implement self-care strategies is that we begin to feel better from the very start. We recognize even a small amount of time and effort will be of benefit. The real challenge is to maintain even the smallest of changes allowing us to build on these to create our optimal and radiant life.

The Soul Chef's Ultimate Challenge

In my first book, *Soul Health: Aligning with Spirit for Radiant Living*, I presented a model – or blueprint – to help understand the key components to leading a healthy life while also facilitating the soul's evolution. You see, as you balance and align the key aspects – or branches – of the human condition, you positively affect your soul as well. In that book, I emphasize the importance of learning to 1) clean out what isn't working, while 2) "filling up" with what would enhance your life. In taking an active approach to both of these steps in our conscious evolution, we ensure our soul evolves.

As you "test" your *Recipe for Radiance*, the process is similar. You will "add a little bit of this" and "take out a little bit of that" along the way. As you grow and change, the ingredients of your *Recipe* will likely shift as well. This is a natural part of the process, and a necessary part of perfecting your soul-care plan as you evolve. Remaining aware of how your needs and resources are shifting will help you to continually "test" your plan to meet your changing needs.

Chapter Twelve

Mastering Your Plate for Ongoing Radiance

"The only recipe is hard work, persistence, and belief."
~ Julen Lopetegui

"Decorating and arranging" your life for radiant living can be fun! Now that you have begun to master the art and soul of self-care, you can start to enjoy your envisioned outcome. This is when you not only imagine your ultimate radiant life, but also get to experience and appreciate your hard work. Good chefs always make sure their meals look and taste great, so sit back and savor the masterpiece you have just created. It is time to enjoy your new sense of balance and fulfillment as you recognize how much better it feels to know and master the art of soul-care.

As you align your life for radiant living, it will continue to taste better and better. Review your recipe card for your own soul-care plan. Add notes for special instructions, "amounts", "duration/frequency", and any other specific information that will help you more clearly identify your *Recipe for Radiance*. Remember, the clearer you are with your recipe now, the easier it will be to implement your soul care plan when needed.

Setting Your Soul's Table

As I mentioned in previous chapters, I started cooking at a very young age, so I already had a basic start to my culinary adventures before beginning 4-H cooking classes in the fourth grade. My teacher encouraged us to enter cooking competitions and one summer I agreed to compete in an event bringing kids together from around the county to prepare and serve their favorite meals. My food received high marks, but the mistakes I made in setting the table made me lose the top award. My family was always rather casual at meals, so I didn't think to study the correct placement of the silverware. If I remember correctly, I reversed the placement of the spoon and fork, a major mistake for judges who cook for a living. All of the pretty linens and flowers in the world could not camouflage misplaced items. I wasn't devastated since it was a fun event, but I did learn a major lesson: "Study, learn, and set your space."

Life is a continual learning process – a constant evolution. In terms of cooking, I couldn't even begin to assess how much I've learned since I first stood on a chair to help my mother in the kitchen. What I do know is I've learned to slow down, study, and remain mindful of how I want to create and present a meal. I've also become more intentional about how I want to lead my life. As far as we know, we are the only species on the planet that can consciously decide to learn and grow. If something is not "right" in our lives, we have the capacity to think ahead, consider our options, and take steps to get moving in the right direction. This may take time and effort, but the very process of learning *IS* the key component of our evolution. Our personal investment to become our own award-winning soul chef is the best way to set our ultimate soul's table.

While the most important part of a meal is the food, chefs also have to consider the presentation of their prized dishes. They determine which plates and dishes will be used, the type of table settings that will enhance their customer's satisfaction, and the special touches such as linens, flowers, and candles that will complete the chef's vision for the perfect dining experience. Many chefs even choose the appropriate tables and chairs to provide a comfortable and sturdy platform on which to offer their culinary art. Master Chefs think of all aspects of the preparation and presentation of food necessary to earn their three-star ratings.

As you become your own master soul chef, you may need some additional tools and "settings" to help you live your radiant life. Many of these tools you may have identified as you created your *Recipe for Radiance*. Here are a few more to consider:

Counseling or Psychotherapy: Many people want to lead more radiant lives, but feel blocked by unresolved issues, concerns, and trauma. If something is getting in the way of allowing you to feel healthy and whole, consider speaking with someone who will help you pave a clearer path to a more fulfilling life. It will be the best investment in *you* that you can ever make.

A health or other certified coach: While therapy is important and even necessary, perhaps you need someone to help you learn to be accountable to yourself. Coaches can assist in helping you establish clear and realistic goals and objectives. In fact, my book coach suggested I write this book after seeing my *Companion Guide* for the *Recipe for Radiance: Mastering the Art and Soul of Self-Care Webinar*. (For more information, go to www.drkatherinetkelly.com and sign up for my newsletter to receive information about upcoming events.)

Online Classes and Webinars: More and more people are turning to the internet to educate themselves about self-care. Thousands of podcasts, classes, and webinars exist to help enhance your life. I offer many online tools as well.

Feel free to check them out on my website (www.drkatherinetkelly.com), follow me on Facebook (www.facebook.com/DrKatherineTKelly/), or join my newsletter community.

Soul-Supportive Products: Whether in need of relaxation supplies, audio recordings, or other self-care products, all you must do is identify what you require and what works best for your particular *Recipe for Radiance.* As mentioned in the early part of this book, I have found aromatherapy and essential oils to be extraordinarily helpful in assisting me in both balancing the various aspects of the human condition and in facilitating my soul's evolution. Just prior to publishing this book, I also launched **Soul Health Essentials**, offering various essential oil blends specifically designed to enhance overall soul health and facilitate personal growth. Go to www.soulhealthessentials.com for more information.

Practitioner Training: "Healer, heal thyself" as they say. If you are a health practitioner of any sort, you need your own supportive services to maintain your most radiant life. Helpers don't always do the best job of helping themselves, so it is particularly important to take care of yourself. Many wonderful practitioner trainings and retreats exist to help professionals be the best they can be so their clientele can reap the most benefit. Consider my ***Soul Health Practitioner Certification*** training if you would like to learn more about how to assist others reach optimal health using the Soul Health Model™. Go to www.drkatherinetkelly.com for more information.

Knowing how to "plate" and "present" your *Recipe for Radiance* will allow you to set a strong foundation for ongoing enjoyment of your newly developed soul-care plan. Remember, reaching optimal health is an ongoing process – one that will benefit you the rest of your life. Once established, never again will you need to determine the key elements of your ultimate self-care.

Now that you have begun a journey to master the art and soul of self-care, you can expect to live a much more fulfilling and radiant life.

Post Script

I'm the first one to admit that self-care takes time and effort. At many points during the writing, editing, and final preparation of this book, I chuckled at the irony of the long and sometimes stressful hours that went into producing a guide to mastering the art and soul of self-care. Although it feeds my soul deeply to help others, my mind and body were often tired and depleted while explaining my metaphor for optimal self-care – the *Recipe for Radiance* – in the last twelve chapters. Even writing these final pages comes at a time when I could use a little R & R.

If you are reading these words, you've made it far enough in the book to show a true commitment to your overall soul-care. You may still question how to create your life-long plan and you may doubt your ability to follow-through. I would be lying if I said this process comes easily. I, too, must sometimes convince myself to stay aligned with what I know will benefit me later. As a human, I may avoid what I know will serve me best, while my soul continues to nudge me to remain invested in the daily nourishment of my soul-care plan. The human and soul sides of me constantly wrestle to see which will prevail, but I've finally gotten to the point of knowing what will happen if I don't choose the soul-care route – I will experience a deep and profound sense of regret. This feeling is a sign that I've gotten off track and need to realign myself for radiant living. Believe me, I know this sense of derailment well, but have learned to use it to motivate me to remain proactive in my own *Recipe for Radiance* whenever possible.

I have two final parting thoughts to share as you embark on your soul-care journey. One is a tip on how to get started while the other provides a way to guarantee you follow through – for the rest of your life! The first will help you overcome the biggest mistake people make when trying to engage in self-care activities. The second will challenge you to expand your understanding of your deepest self – your soul – so you truly embrace the importance of self-care on your evolutionary path.

What is the biggest mistake people when it comes to self-care? Strangely enough, they don't take the "self" in self-care seriously. They don't reach deeply enough into their soul to determine what *they* really need in order to rebalance or restore their lives. They rely on what others tell them then fall short in nourishing themselves at the deepest level.

Until now, no one has written a book that helps you understand self-care really is soul-care. After reading the *Recipe for Radiance*, you now have the essential tools to create your life-long soul care plan. Remember, the soul is the essence of who you are and if you don't stop long enough to listen, identify, and act on what your soul needs, you won't master the art of self-care. You will focus only on the action and not the outcome – and thus fail to create the radiant life that is rightfully yours.

Most people who struggle with motivation to engage in self-care behaviors do so because they center their attention on the effort it will take to participate in these activities, rather than on the effect that will follow. They talk themselves out of partaking in nourishing behaviors before they have the chance to "taste" the final product. This is an action based in the human condition, not of the soul. The soul's most natural state is radiant and light, but we only experience this state of being when we have fully nourished our innermost ally. By becoming your own soul chef, you will ensure that you live a more radiant life. So, to overcome the biggest mistake people make in self-care, you must put the "self" back into the care.

The second parting thought I'd like to share relates to the idea of self-love. In the revised second edition of my book, *Soul Health: Aligning with Spirit for Radiant Living*, I added an entire chapter about the importance of loving yourself to create a more radiant life. You see, you won't plan, let alone execute soul-care activities if you don't love yourself enough to do so. In that book, I wrote about my father's accident that occurred when I was nine years old. After watching his twelve-year decline and subsequent death, I came to realize his demise occurred primarily due to a profound lack of self-love. There was no physical reason he couldn't take care of himself—he just didn't love himself enough to do it.

As I talk to clients about both self-care and soul health, I emphasize that self-love is the essential ingredient in aligning their lives for radiant living. You must love yourself enough to take the time to identify what your soul needs to thrive, as well as invest in yourself enough to follow through. A strong sense of self-love guarantees a life-long commitment to your soul-care plan. Without this key ingredient, your *Recipe for Radiance* will lack the essence necessary to create life-long radiance.

Simply stated, putting the "self" back into care requires us to also put the "self" back into love. Since self-care *IS* soul-care, this means it is time to lovingly put the soul back into your daily life. It is time to reacquaint yourself with the essence of who you are to create your most optimal and radiant life. In this way, "soul food" takes on a whole new meaning. This term no longer applies just to a type of southern cuisine, it now encompasses a whole new – and more radiant – way to experience life. By getting to know your soul and learning to feed it, you guarantee a rich and nourishing evolutionary path.

Self-care is a journey. Your personalized *Recipe for Radiance* feeds a party of one – *you*. You are your own VIP customer and it is now up to you to feast on your optimal life. Like any chef, you will experiment with new flavors and ingredients along the way. But you have now earned the title of Executive Chef of your Soul.

Here's to the most important feast of your life!

References and Suggested Reading

American Institute of Stress. 2019. "The Holmes-Rahe Stress Inventory." Accessed March 2019. https://www.stress.org/holmes-rahe-stress-inventory.

EProvide. 2019. "Stress Vulnerability Scale (SVS)." Accessed March 2019. https://eprovide.mapi-trust.org/instruments/stress-vulnerability-scale.

Holmes, T. H. & Rahe, R. H. 1967. The social readjustment rating scale. *Journal of Psychosomatic Research,* 11(2), 213-218.

Lally, van Jaarsveld, Potts & Wardle. 2009. How are habits formed: Modelling habit formation in the real world. *European Journal of Social Psychology*, 40(6), 998-1009.

Made in the USA
Columbia, SC
02 May 2019